S0-BLQ-769

GETTING GROW ROOMS RIGHT

EVERYTHING YOU NEED TO KNOW ABOUT HVAC DESIGN, SPECIFICATION, SELECTION, INSTALLATION, AND OPERATION

Geoff Brown with Dan Dettmers

Getting Grow Rooms Right

Published by Dehumidified Air Solutions
Montreal, Canada
AgronomicIQ.com

Disclaimer: The statements made in this book are intended as general guidance regarding HVAC application for grow rooms and to spark thought and discussion around what solutions may be best for growers in a general sense. The content of this book cannot be taken as direct advice applicable to any specific project. The author and publisher do not assume and hereby disclaim any liability to any party for any loss, damage or disruption caused by errors or omissions, whether such errors or omissions result from negligence, accident or any other cause. This book is not a substitute for professional and competent HVAC advice from relevant professionals such as engineers and equipment manufacturers.

Credits:
Edited by Devyn Barrie
Designed by Heather Morin
Additional direction by Steve MacDonald, Deanna White, Daniel Kerr, and Derrick Simpson.

ISBN: 978-1-9992746-0-3

Printed in Canada

CONTENTS

ABOUT THE AUTHORS

GEOFF BROWN
DIRECTOR, AGRONOMIC IQ

Geoff Brown got his start in the HVAC industry in the shop of Seresco Dehumidifiers, a company founded in 2003. He quickly gained a hands-on understanding of precision HVAC equipment by helping to build the very units that would later be installed at indoor pools across North America.

He later became a regional sales manager for Seresco, where he worked for several years on a variety of indoor pool dehumidification projects of all sizes, honing his expertise on applied thermodynamics and HVAC application.

Geoff became interested in the emerging field of commercial cannabis growing and was selected to help launch a new division to serve the market, called Agronomic IQ, offering the most advanced temperature and humidity control equipment in the grow room industry. The brand launched in September 2018, after extensive research into the HVAC needs of the marketplace and development of purpose-built solutions to address those needs.

As one of North America's leading authorities on HVAC for grow rooms, Geoff participates in various advisory boards in the cannabis industry and is a contributing member to The American Society of Agricultural and Biological Engineers (ASABE) X653 guideline *"Heating, Ventilating, and Air*

Conditioning (HVAC) for Indoor Plant Environments without Sunlight."

Geoff is also a frequent keynote speaker across North America, educating growers and engineers about successful HVAC design, specification, selection, and installation for indoor farming and grow rooms. In his spare time, he tours Canada for regional and national dodgeball tournaments.

Geoff Brown
Contact@AgronomicIQ.com
1.833.327.2447

DAN DETTMERS APPLICATIONS ENGINEER, QUEST DEHUMIDIFIERS

Dan Dettmers is an Applications Engineer at Quest Dehumidifiers and their Controlled Environmental Agriculture divisions of Quest and Agronomic IQ. Before Quest Dehumidifiers, Mr. Dettmers dedicated over 20 years to research and instruction at University of Wisconsin-Madison, primarily in industrial refrigeration for food and pharmaceutical processing.

Additionally, he was a founder of Gorst Valley Hops and Bine Implement, where he developed disruptive technology to dry hops (Cannabaceae Humulus lupulus) at ambient temperatures for improved preservation of terpenes, aroma, and flavor.

Within the HVAC&R industry, Mr. Dettmers has chaired and served on multiple Standing and Technical Committees in ASHRAE, including development of ASHRAE's Position Documents on Natural Refrigerants, Ozone Depleting Substances and Ammonia as a Refrigerant.

In his current role, Mr. Dettmers leads efforts to develop more efficient methods for handling latent loads and improving the air quality for Cannabis and all Controlled Environmental Agriculture operations. He is a contributing member to ASABE X653 guideline *"Heating, Ventilating, and Air Conditioning (HVAC) for Indoor Plant Environments without Sunlight."*

Dan Dettmers
Sales@QuestClimate.com
1.877.420.1330

AUTHOR'S NOTE

Until you've written a book, few people realize how much time and effort goes into the process. And there are times when you ask yourself, what have I bitten off here? But persevere we did, because this information is desperately needed by so many folks in the grow room industry.

Fortunately for me, I was surrounded by a team of people dedicated to our mission of helping to solve one of the most pressing challenges in this industry. For starters...

Devyn, our writer and editor: We (most importantly, I) couldn't have completed this project without your tireless effort. If you are ever looking for someone capable of simultaneously articulating your most complicated thoughts and slicing you to pieces with his quick wit and fearless tongue, he has my wholehearted endorsement. I owe you a no-name beer or two.

Steve: Your marketing and brand strategy genius has brought us enough success and reach to pull off a project like this. My hats off to you. On top of that, your marketing team — led by Deanna with Dan Kerr and Derrick — have had the patience and good nature to deal with the inevitable delays and frustrations caused by non-writers writing a book and coordinating the final details of typesetting, line edits, and printing. A kick-ass bunch of people.

Clif: Your guidance in navigating the much larger organization I now find myself in has been invaluable, and I look forward to continuing to extract as much of your experience as possible. I'm sorry when I'm being a stubborn pain, and I promise that I'm actually listening and learning. Don't give up on me!

To the core of my day-to-day team, Steph, Adria, Mark, and Jason: You have been incredible and stepped up when needed, working hard and long hours to keep us all motivated. We've had a crazy year and I'm excited to continue growing personally and professionally with you all.

And last, but certainly not least: You, our readers. It's a once in a lifetime opportunity to be involved as we are in an emerging market, and we are incredibly fortunate that the people working to drive this industry forward are such a pleasure to work and interact with: the manufacturers, engineers, architects, investors, contractors, and most importantly, you, the growers. I could not be luckier, and I hope that you all recognize how cool this industry is and how awesome it is to be involved in this market.

We hope that you find the information in this book extremely valuable. We'd be delighted to hear from you with any questions or suggestions for additional content, because I expect we'll continue to update the book with at least a 2nd edition as this industry continues to grow and change.

Geoff Brown
Director
Agronomic IQ

INTRODUCTION

This book was written out of pure necessity for a simple and accessible reference guide for all in the cultivation industry as they seek the right growing environment for cannabis.

Although modern cannabis culture is mostly borne out of the 1960s, humans have been using cannabis for thousands of years for adult and medicinal purposes. Some of the earliest evidence found to-date shows that cannabis with high THC levels was used for rituals in western China as early as 500 B.C.

Since then, its use and attitudes towards its use have shifted among different societies. From its origins in open fields during simpler times, to moving underground to grow in basements or garages during periods of prohibition in some cultures, the story of cannabis is one of continuous evolution.

Today, with its legalization for adult and medical use in Canada, plus a growing number of U.S. states, cannabis is in the midst of a rebirth. No longer a black market, the grow industry has become legitimate seemingly overnight.

Few industries experience such rapid expansion. Fewer still experience this expansion while shifting from illegal to legitimate. Countless growers have appeared in the marketplace, all of them looking to build a brand with a quality product. So far, approaches to producing crops at scale have varied wildly, with everyone going out their own way to discover the secret sauce. There is no "beaten path" here, as no standards have yet been set. And, for those who have discovered what works, they aren't sharing it in this highly competitive and secretive landscape. Thus, there is little opportunity to learn from each other's mistakes.

Certainly, there is no shortage of mistakes being made. Sadly, this is the by-product of industrial secrecy in pursuit of competitive advantage. Growers are making big decisions about, and major investments in, their new facilities without the benefit of a complete understanding of what's needed to make them work. As a result, they are getting stuck with underperforming HVAC equipment and systems that do not deliver the kind of consistent and quality crop they need to succeed in the marketplace. Growers know a lot about the plant but have not had the opportunity to finesse their knowledge about the other aspects critical to growing the plant in a controlled environment.

Why is this happening? How can we stop the vicious cycle from repeating? This book is intended to address these two questions and provide the much-needed insights that many growers are missing. This book asks many questions about certain aspects of the industry and examines how positive change could serve everyone much better. We discuss how current practices can be changed and encourage the reader to ask themselves how they can progress as well.

You probably picked up this book because you're involved in some way with the grow industry. Whether you're an architect or engineer, an executive, grow master, operator, or contractor, we hope you will find some useful takeaways in this book.

We're Agronomic IQ, manufacturer of the smartest and most advanced grow room HVAC equipment in North America, and a member of Dehumidified Air Solutions, the leading provider of dehumidification systems. In more than 40 years of dealing with indoor pools, we have acquired the most expansive and detailed knowledge base of dehumidification technology and engineering of any company in the HVAC industry and have long shared this knowledge with the indoor pool industry. With grow room conditions posing many of the same challenges as indoor pools, we're looking forward to continuing these efforts for cannabis growers.

Some may be unfamiliar with our Agronomic IQ brand. We entered the market in September 2018, deliberately late. We took our time and studied the landscape before getting involved in HVAC solutions for cannabis growing because we wanted to watch and learn from the mistakes of others in trying to apply their solutions. By learning the market first, we've had much better results early on. This experience has allowed our team to witness the successes, and the mistakes, that make or break modern grow rooms. We wrote this book to share our dehumidification experience and wisdom so that others can avoid the errors that would ruin their facility. This guide has the potential to help everyone involved in the industry.

We recognize that getting the right growing environment is challenging. There are many variables to consider that affect plant growth, plus critical ancillary factors like capital and operating costs, return on investment, energy usage and, of course, profit.

The business case for proper environment control in a grow room is obvious, with serious implications for crop quality and consistency, as well as safety. A poorly controlled space could become toxic for plants and can lead to a reduced yield, damage to plants, or even the entire loss of a crop. These negative outcomes have serious implications for the brand image and market position of growers.

Discerning cannabis customers today have a wide choice in the marketplace. They expect quality and consistency. As many growers are looking for exclusivity agreements with retailers, being unable to deliver on these could make business very difficult.

But while delivering a good product experience is paramount to growers, they also have limited financial resources for buying, installing, and operating equipment. Understanding the options available helps growers make the right decision on this point and benefit from equipment payback.

Because we know HVAC, this book mainly focuses on that critical topic, while touching on other relevant issues, such as lighting types and their energy consumption. We've only written about what we know in this book; there is no conjecture, only facts. You also won't find any sales pitches in these pages.

The book begins with more context about the grow industry's evolution and its position today. You'll also learn about the economics of growing and how to achieve equipment Return on Investment (ROI). Read about the most serious mistakes made in the design and operation of current facilities, how you can avoid them for yourself, and get the best possible grow conditions for the lowest cost in HVAC equipment purchase, operation, and maintenance.

Not everything in this book is for every reader. But every reader will find something in this book — a useful takeaway, a new perspective they didn't think about, or even an eye-opening discovery.

We hope you will find it a useful resource.

Disclaimer: We use specific, and sometimes absolute, language in a world where no standards or absolutes exist. The concepts presented in this book are intended to be 100% sound and useful for the reader; however, please note that we are speaking about what we notice most often, not what's being applied in every case or with every client we encounter.

— *Geoff Brown*

ICONS USED IN THIS BOOK

Key information of interest especially to those who own and operate grow room facilities.

Important details every engineer should know before designing a grow room.

Useful information and tips particularly relevant to contractors involved in grow room HVAC projects.

Tips that may be useful to many different groups of readers.

Important concepts for those not deeply familiar with the grow industry.

INTRODUCTION TO THE GROW INDUSTRY

CHAPTER 01

The North American cannabis industry, borne out of recent legalization in Canada and some U.S. states, is not really a "new" industry. It's more of a rebirth and commercialization of what has existed for generations.

Over the past few centuries, the production of cannabis in North America has gone from outdoor hemp farms that were a key part of the region's early economy during colonization, to underground indoor growing of cannabis for use during periods of prohibition, to the legitimate scaled-up indoor cultivation of the modern day. Just as the methods of production have evolved and changed over time, so have the attitudes about and use of cannabis. Recently, there has been a relaxation of public opinion towards cannabis, initially for medical use and more recently for adult use. This growing acceptance of cannabis is one of the primary factors that resulted in governments changing course to now legalize what was criminalized.

The cannabis business today is in a whirlwind expansion as legalization sweeps the continent. As of mid-2019, 33 U.S. states plus the District of Columbia, Puerto Rico, Guam, the U.S. Virgin Islands and the Northern Mariana Islands have legalized cannabis for at least medical use. Eleven states, and the District of Columbia, have legalization for adult use. North of the border, Canada legalized in the fall of 2018.

Tens of thousands of businesses are involved in the multibillion-dollar industry on both sides of the border. The U.S. legal market size in 2018 was pegged at US$11.9 billion by Grand View Research, who suggested it could expand at a compound annual growth rate of 24.1% between 2019 and 2025. Most of the market share was attributed to medical cannabis; however, the adult use market is expected to become the fastest-growing segment.[1]

The rapid growth curve has attracted billions of dollars of investment and, with many cannabis companies now publicly traded, opportunities to profit from this sector are now available to anyone.

CANNABIS IN THE NEW WORLD

Looking back through history, European explorers introduced cannabis to the New World sometime around 1606, when it was planted in Port Royal, Acadia (modern-day Nova Scotia).[2]

Although some say cannabis existed in North America prior to the arrival of Europeans, it is improbable that whatever was growing here was the same type of plant. Cannabis plants, in fact, seem to have originated from Asia many thousands of years ago and were used for medical and psychoactive purposes.[3] The stories of cannabis already growing in North America are likely an extension of mistaken early sightings by explorers like Jacques Cartier, who had apparently described seeing the land "frill of hempe." It is now known that he actually saw some strain of "Indian hemp," which is similar to, but distinct from, the hemp plant known as cannabis sativa L.[4] In the early days of the New World, cannabis, or more specifically, hemp, was used for textile purposes.

Hemp was a key part of the New Word's economy. It was so useful, in fact, that Britain required farmers in its colonies to grow hemp or face a fine.[5] The French also produced large quantities of hemp. They took to mass cultivating and exporting hemp, and at one point were selling two million pounds per year to England.[6] Hemp was used in the New World for centuries right up until it was eventually outlawed. It was widely used for textile purposes and was the material of choice for rope in both nations' navies.

Cannabis was not used in North America for its psychoactive properties until at least the late nineteenth century, according to a Library of Parliament report prepared for the Senate of Canada in 2002.[7] In fact, according to Barney Warf, a professor of geography and atmospheric science at the University of Kansas who tracked the geographical movement of cannabis throughout history, the use of cannabis for such purposes was first introduced to the U.S. around 1910.[3] People who emigrated from Mexico during the revolution arrived in the U.S. and were known to smoke cannabis. Negative racial attitudes toward the Mexican refugees eventually led to the drug's outlaw, Warf wrote in his peer-reviewed report. By the late 1930s in the U.S., all forms of cannabis, including hemp, were outlawed. (Canada had begun prohibition of cannabis in the early 1920s, although adult use of the drug was notably less pronounced north of the border, according to the Library of Parliament/Senate of Canada report.)

GOING UNDERGROUND

By the time prohibition began in the U.S., the idea of adult-use cannabis was not novel. "Reefer," as it was called in contemporary slang, had very much entered the popular culture. In 1932, Cab Calloway sang about the "Reefer Man." By 1936, the "dope epidemic" had so concerned government officials that they produced the movie "Reefer Madness," filled with sensationalized situations where cannabis caused mayhem and tragedy, intended to scare young people away from trying it. Regardless, use of the substance continued. Even celebrities were known to enjoy it; rumors circulated that the reason famed swing drummer Gene Krupa was able to play his solos for so long and with so much energy was because he would get high before a show (he denied that was the case). In 1943, he was arrested and convicted for sending a minor to his hotel room to grab some joints for him; Krupa was fined $500 and served 90 days in jail.[8]

It would be decades before cannabis could be viably grown indoors. Prior to the 1970s, most of North America's cannabis supply came from Mexico, according to the Globe and Mail.[9] The indoor growing revolution began when Mexico began exterminating these crops at the request of the Reagan administration in the U.S. in the 1980s.

The move underground prompted some changes in the type of plant.

Cannabis sativa, popular for the invigorating kind of effects it produces, which can be paired with social occasions, is difficult to grow in cold climates. Cannabis indica could be grown up north, but it tends to sedate users. Indoor growing allowed new engineering on the plants that enabled growers to create hybrids.

Additionally, indoor growing led to the rise of sensimilla plants, the exclusive harvest of female plants that have not been pollinated by a male plant. The shift toward sensimilla has led to a gradual increase in the average THC content of crops. One study found the average THC content of black-market cannabis seized between 1995 and 2014 had increased from 4% to 12%.[10]

Technological advances made indoor growing more viable through the 1980s. New types of lighting, such as metal-halide and high-pressure sodium vapor bulbs contributed to the trend, the *Globe and Mail* reported.[9] As indoor growing continued, growers learned that they could control their crops to reach desired levels of quality and consistency. These indoor grows, as they continue today, were of significantly better quality than what had been growing in open fields. But they were still limited by several factors.

For one, many growers were still DIYers with limited technical knowledge. These pioneer growers operated their grow from home, usually in a shed, garage, or basement. Although there were certainly large-scale, commercial grows, the vast majority of indoor cannabis in the black market was grown by pioneers in this way.

Much of their understanding of plant science came from learning as they went, often by trial and error. In more recent times, with internet forums and social media, information on how to have a successful grow has become easier to share, so the DIYers of today are far ahead of the pioneers of the last few decades.

The pioneer growers were wary of being caught. Tolerance for these grow-ops has always been low among authorities, so their operators had to fly under the radar. This necessitated small-scale operations that used a minimum of electricity and did not involve large equipment, which significantly limited the output they could produce.

One of the biggest red flags to tip off authorities was large electricity use. The lighting systems use substantial power, as does HVAC. Most growers cannot load out on the equipment they know would lead to better grows because it would likely result in them getting caught. Some industrious growers in the black market — usually those connected to organized crime — buy entire houses to convert to grow-ops, including lamp arrays and plug-in dehumidifiers and fans. Upgrading the central HVAC is out of the question as a commercial-grade air conditioner for a house would obviously raise some eyebrows. These grow-ops are often discovered by authorities because of their huge energy demand. Additionally, the heat generated by the lights often means they are the only house on the block during winter with no snow on the roof. Resale of these houses is very difficult, in part, because of non-code wiring modifications made to accommodate high wattage lights and damage due to high humidity levels.

Most pioneer growers made do with small lamps and whatever HVAC equipment they could slap together from the hardware store. Usually, this was limited to small windowsill air conditioners and plug-in dehumidifiers of about 60- or 80-pints capacity. This limited the number of plants that could be produced per square foot. Indoor growing technology had hit its limit.

CANNABIS BECOMES LEGITIMIZED

Although decriminalization in some states began as early as the 1970s, legalization took much longer. The first North American law to legalize cannabis for any personal use was Proposition 215 in California, a ballot measure approved in 1996. This law permitted medical use of cannabis, and for individuals or caregivers to cultivate the plant for that use only. The law did not set up a regulatory framework for a legal medical cannabis market, so black markets in California continued. Partial implementation of the proposition came with the aptly named California Senate Bill 420, which established a medical marijuana program.

Over time, more states legalized for medical use. Later, some added legalization for adult use as well. The first adult use legalizations came in 2012 with Colorado and Washington states.

The legal cannabis industry, which started in the small-scale to serve the medical market, was now in the big leagues. The market, worth hundreds of millions in its early medical-only stage, was quickly becoming worth billions.

Suddenly, the landscape changed. Big corporate money is coming into the picture and the small growers are fading away and being replaced by large companies, some of them publicly traded and with big market capitalizations. Some of the pioneer growers are finding work with these big companies as experienced plant specialists, or even becoming major shareholders in them. Others have founded their own cannabis companies.

The growers working for these companies are now called "master growers," and they're bringing their years of experience in cultivation to realize hopefully big profits. Who knew growing cannabis in your basement could eventually make you a millionaire?

THE DIFFICULTY IN SCALING UP

These small-scale growers-turned pros are now coming up against new challenges posed by scaling up. They are learning and adapting their plant-growing skills to a new industry that bears little resemblance to the conditions they were working in before.

The difference is in the facilities used to produce cannabis today. They are vastly different in most ways from the grow-ops of before. The thinking that informed a small basement grow-op is not applying well to the modern-day grow facilities that are hundreds or thousands of times larger.

As a result, some mistakes have been made in the new landscape. Not all of them have been made by the growers, however. In this industry, with so many new people getting involved, there's understandably some unfamiliarity with all the intricacies that go into cannabis cultivation.

The reason for the mistakes trickles down from legalization. The laws allowing cannabis are, in fact, the catalyst for some of the very expensive false moves in the industry today. How? Because to build these new growing facilities, the engineering community has become involved. After all, you can't get a building permit from the city without a professional engineer. But few engineers know about cultivation and most do not have actual experience in this field. As a result, engineers applied theories and technologies from other applications they were familiar with to grow facilities, many of which have underperformed.

> Engineers aren't the only new people to the party. Numerous third parties like equipment vendors and consultants are also trying to get a slice of the action. Again, not everyone getting involved has a ton of expertise in this unique field, so it's no surprise mistakes get made.

You would think there would be lessons learned during 25 years of growing medical cannabis. A lot has changed in the last two decades, but it's still the wild west out there. The engineering and horticultural industries have yet to establish standards, and information is still minimally shared. Many growers are keeping their hard-won expertise to themselves as a competitive advantage. This means lessons learned, for the most part, do not propagate to the rest of the industry.

In this wild and confusing business, experts are hard to identify. Grow masters, with their hands-on knowledge about plants, are experts at growing. But they're still learning about modern HVAC and building controls, key pieces of technology that have a critical impact on the success of a grow facility, regardless of size.

Systems are available today that can coordinate all key controls for maximum control and variability. For example, building automation software can send signals to controllers for lighting, watering, and the HVAC system to initiate automatic adjustments to required conditions depending on grow stage or whether the lights are on or off. Many of the manual operations can now be handled by intelligent systems, but this technology is new and unfamiliar. Many growers and controls vendors are still learning how to implement technologies effectively.

New approaches are required for the modern-day grow room, some of which go counter to what both growers and the engineering community expect.

The good news is that, with all the new corporate investments, untold resources are now available for companies to discover innovative new ways to solve the traditional challenges of indoor growing. As a result, the industry is in a state of constant innovation and growth. Their scale is no longer limited by the risk of detection or DIY resources. Some very smart and capable people in the industry right now are achieving amazing results with technology.

One example of a new technology applied to the grow industry is LED lighting. One of the common problems for indoor growing, as mentioned earlier, is the heavy electricity use and heat generation of traditional lighting solutions. A 2014 review by the Northwest Power and Conservation Council determined that the average facility in Washington state used 38% of its total electricity consumption to power the lights. Also, about 80% of total electricity use was attributable to the lights, including indirect causes such as heavier load on cooling equipment due to heat emitted from the lights.[11]

As a solution to this challenge, significant research and development is invested into LED lights. They are more expensive at the outset than other types of lights, but their overall cost of ownership is demonstrably lower over time. Just in the past few years, LED lighting has been on the rise and that trend can be expected to continue in the near term.

However, where is the research and development for HVAC solutions? So far, there has not been much. The industry has continued using essentially the same equipment solutions that were applied 30 years ago to basement grow-ops in the 1980s. For the most part, this means standard air conditioners for cooling and low-capacity portable dehumidifiers for humidity control.

The industry is adapting, learning, and growing very quickly. At the present time, it remains in a late-stage of the shift from pioneer to professional, small-scale to industrial-scale operations. Growing pains are natural in any industry, especially one that's grown up so rapidly. With continued attention towards finding new approaches, the future for modern-day grow rooms is very positive.

CONCLUSION

The cannabis industry as it exists today is not so much a new industry, but rather one that has existed in many different forms over several centuries and is currently in a state of rapid change. Cannabis is no longer produced in small basement grow-ops, but has become an industry made up of large companies, many of them publicly traded, that are constructing massive new facilities to grow cannabis on an industrial scale.

But while these new facilities are being built, countless mistakes continue to be made. Growers are realizing they cannot apply the traditional methods of pioneer grow-ops to these modern facilities. New and innovative solutions are required, but reaching them is hampered by the fact that very few people involved in the industry have the knowledge and expertise needed to find these solutions. Growers are experts at cultivating plants, but they don't necessarily know much about modern HVAC or building controls. Many engineers and equipment vendors who are now included in new projects are missing key insights into cannabis growing that could help them significantly.

GROW ROOMS TODAY: A NEW DAWN

CHAPTER 02

Just as the cannabis industry has grown at a rapid rate over the past five years, the grow room environment has also experienced significant evolution.

As mentioned in the last chapter, growers have progressed from amateur to pro, seemingly overnight. As they seek to produce massive harvests and secure a place in the market, they're coming up against several major challenges associated with producing at-scale. This is a new frontier for many and a new field that requires different ways of thinking: novel solutions, many of which are unfamiliar to both long-time growers and the new entrants into the industry such as engineers and equipment vendors.

The four key challenges of scaling up in this landscape are:

- **A lack of experience across multiple domains.**
- **Market and regulatory pressures.**
- **Lack of standards.**
- **Misapplication of traditional equipment.**

New approaches are required for the modern-day grow room, some of which run counter to the knowledge and practice of both growers and the engineering community.

LACK OF EXPERIENCE ACROSS MULTIPLE DOMAINS

There are severe knowledge gaps in this industry that need to be closed before it can truly progress and mature.

The issue is not necessarily knowledge related to cultivation. As noted, master growers are experts when it comes to growing cannabis. Some of them were once amateur growers operating out of their basement or small-footprint operations, others have PhDs in related fields, and now they're bringing their world-class knowledge to a newly legitimized market as employees, shareholders, executives, or even founders of new cannabis companies. Naturally, any industry that started in a basement is bound to experience some growing pains.

We want to highlight the knowledge that is missing or inconsistent regarding how to best scale up the production environment. The ideas that applied well to basement grow-ops are not applying well to commercial indoor grow facilities, something the industry is discovering through great pain and expense.

Lack of understanding also persists among those who are ancillary to the industry, such as third-party equipment suppliers. Manufacturers are paying serious attention to the grow industry these days, as they hope to provide some much-needed solutions to many of the challenges facing growers. Solutions lead to bigger profits and the possibility of significant repeat business.

But getting traditional suppliers involved with the cannabis industry has its risks. It's a mixed bag: you could benefit, or you could lose. They don't all necessarily understand the growing environment. On top of that, growers — who do understand — are now dealing with products and services they never had to before, or at a scale they never dealt with before. The result is confusion, poor communication, and poor implementation of proposed solutions that often don't hit the mark.

> Select and work with manufacturers who know the industry and offer products that are purpose-built for cannabis growing.

The inconsistency of knowledge has led to major harm, especially to growers in new markets who are scaling up to meet the demands of the market and investors looking for outsized returns on investment before commoditization at massive volume. Facilities of a million or more square feet are under construction and huge amounts of money are being poured into these developments. But with technology and knowledge in its infancy, it is an open question whether those dollars are being invested intelligently and put towards a facility that will work and deliver value.

MARKET AND REGULATORY PRESSURES

Pressures related to the market or regulations are a very modern challenge facing growers. Obviously, under the black market, someone growing cannabis in their basement did not have to worry about following government regulations. Additionally, there were very few market pressures for them to worry about as they most often had a captive customer base: as long as their prices were reasonable, clients were not likely to seek out another supplier.

The legal market has brought about a new landscape that changes the game dramatically.

Many growers are now large, publicly traded companies with regulated facilities and some transparency requirements, including quarterly releases of financial results. Producers are also typically expected to publish in their quarterly reports the grow yields they are achieving. There is a pressure to improve financial results on a quarter-to-quarter basis, and investors want to see maximized production at all facilities as quickly as possible.

The public nature of these companies means more diverse types of investors who hold stocks in them. Many of the new investors on the scene have less patience than the early venture capitalists or angel investors. Many investors now expect a certain level of market maturity in the cannabis industry, but that market maturity is still evolving. The industry is simply too new to expect anything else. However, with many growers relying on investors to supply the capital needed to take on the market and build up, falling short of expectations is not an option.

Cannabis markets are unpredictable and rapidly evolving. Any new markets under development, which is most of them, are experiencing major supply shortages because few were prepared to meet the tremendous demand among people in areas where cannabis has become legal for adult and medical use. The demand is driving the pace of facility development to dizzying levels as growers, seeing an opportunity to grab market share early on, scale up. By offering a large supply and brand recognition in markets where there is little product available, growers improve their chances of gaining large market share at an early stage, which has strong business and strategic value.

But the execution must be done properly. For one, they need to be able to consistently produce by avoiding mistakes that could lose crop or create inconsistent product. They also need to ensure quality and consistency even as they attempt to grow more crop, more quickly. After all, it's not much good to build a reputation for being a bad or inconsistent producer. Once more supply is available, all your hard-won customers will flee for better product!

It is critical that growers scale up the right way. This is no area for a "rush job." The idiom "buy once, cry once" applies well here: while it is slower and more expensive at first to take the time and care to do this right, you'll save more in the long run by avoiding headaches and unnecessary ownership costs.

Adding to this pressure, the varying regulatory environments are also challenging growers.

Some regulatory set-ups may make business less flexible and require different approaches. For example, some may require a full grow to be evaluated before the producer can receive a production permit. To minimize their capital exposure early on, the grower might be motivated to build a small first stage of their facility simply to satisfy this licensing requirement. After they go through the required harvests and receive the permit, the facility can be expanded to accommodate full production. This is a good example of how local regulations can have an impact on all aspects of growing, because the scale affects the HVAC system type and design. Some types of HVAC systems are not conducive to incremental expansion. The ideal HVAC solution is one that can cost-effectively scale with additional rooms or square footage.

Another example of regulatory pressures relates to the economics of growing in each given market. Some markets that have low barrier of entry for growers and do not limit the number of licenses are producing the opposite of a supply shortage; they have created an enormous glut. These markets are at or near saturation, causing the market price per gram to drop. This supply results in even more pressure for growers to cut costs and offer cheaper products. In a saturated market, one of the drivers of success for a producer is lower cost.

The economics of growing is discussed further in the next chapter, but the key takeaway is that your choice of HVAC equipment can vary significantly depending on variables like the size of your company, your location, and your regulatory landscape. These factors further contribute to challenges in the new frontier of growing at-scale.

LACK OF STANDARDS

One of the main reasons for the lack of consistent knowledge in the grow industry is because there are no standards in place regarding buildings and their systems. This gap is seriously hurting the industry right now by contributing to the information vacuum.

Standards are important for any industry because they help ensure the right solutions are applied, developed and agreed upon by those involved in the sector. The cannabis industry does not yet have any standards for buildings and systems, which makes the design process more challenging.

In the mainstream, engineers rely on proven and documented standards in order to properly handle buildings they are not familiar with. For example, the codes published by the American Society of Heating, Refrigeration and Air Conditioning Engineers (ASHRAE), are well-defined standards relating to built environments and are applied in all kinds of buildings across North America, as well as implemented as the basis for countless local building codes. ASHRAE's handbook has been published for many years with continual updating, with the earliest version dating to the 1920s.

However, ASHRAE's codes are geared towards residential and commercial buildings that are primarily designed for humans. There currently are no ASHRAE standards that relate directly to indoor plant environments and few of their standards are sufficient to address the unique needs and demands of these spaces.

In the hyper-competitive grow industry, even those who think they have found the answers to these challenges are not inclined to share information or insights. This "secret sauce" mentality has exacerbated the challenges by ensuring that very little research or data-sharing occurs in the industry. If this secrecy continues, there is little hope for developing industry standards and best practices.

As a result, engineers are without guidance when they get involved in the design and construction of modern grow rooms. They are forced to improvise and feel their way along. They wind up inventing solutions based largely on guesswork and the application of best practices from other environments or industries. The result is a bit like trying to put a square peg in a round hole: it doesn't quite fit.

Standards in any industry are critical. They are a set of principles that everyone has agreed on and can be followed uniformly to ensure ideal outcomes. As the International Standards Organization says, standards answer the important question: "What is the best way of doing this?"

Countless industries before have faced a similar challenge and wound up developing their own sets of standards. Such progress is the mark of a maturing industry and serves many useful purposes.

One key benefit of standards is that they reduce risk for businesses. As companies in the grow industry navigate their way to market, they need a clear set of guidelines to streamline the process and minimize false moves. Investments can be made with more confidence, knowing there is a body of work that backs up any decisions. This foundation provides a clear sense of direction for executives and investors, as well as people directly involved in projects, like engineers. All parties involved would benefit from learning strategies to repeat success and create consistent and sustainable outcomes, something that's good for everyone!

> By seeking out the best standards, the grow industry can benefit from improved business economics, higher efficiency, better ROI, and a reduced environmental footprint.

Standards also provide a framework for innovation. As the British Standards Institution says, agreed-upon guidelines establish "rules of the game" by "defining common vocabularies, establishing the essential characteristics of a product or service, and by identifying the best practice within the ecosystems that will ensure successful outcomes." Most relevant for the grow business is that standards allow everyone to identify the main issues and then work together to find solutions. This process is especially critical in the early stages of a new business ecosystem, which is exactly where this industry sits at the present day.

While innovation exists to a great degree in the current industry, it would benefit from the kind of scope and direction that comes from having a set of standards in place. Standards could signal to ancillary manufacturers exactly what the market needs and remove the guesswork involved in providing it by breaking down communication barriers.

You may think some standards would have been created in the 25 years of medical cannabis. While it's certainly true that some things have changed since that industry began, the experience of the industry has not necessarily translated into formalized guidelines. Nor would those standards reflect the extraordinary advancements made in industry technologies just in the past couple of years. The main standards emerging from medical grows are governmental regulations relating to quality of crop and specific chemical contents, such as level of CBD vs. THC. But these are of little help to someone building a new operation today with questions relating to facility design and operation. Earlier medical grows are not necessarily similar to those being built today, especially for adult use grows, which, as a reminder, are expected to be the fastest-growing market segment in cannabis for the next few years.

The game is different now. A lot of medical cannabis operations from before were at a lower scale than what growers want to accomplish today with adult use crops and medical crops.

While the plant is similar, and the facility operates in much the same ways, we know the scale is much larger and that presents its own challenges.

The nature of medical grows is quite different than adult use grows, and this difference can have consequences in the cost of designing and operating a grow room. For example, medical cannabis operations and products are typically regulated very tightly by both the grower and government.

Medical grows must follow a different set of regulatory requirements and potentially more stringent testing. Medical crop must be very consistent because successful patient outcomes depend on it. People usually choose their medical product based on trial and error. Once they find a good solution, they stick with it and expect that it will be regularly available and provide the same results every time. This quality control is obviously important for both the patient's health, consistency of medicinal benefits, as well as the grower's business success.

Adult use cannabis grown at scale similarly must be consistent, but its needs are driven more by the brand and its target market, rather than certain regulations.

A facility for adult use grows may have different requirements for its design than a medical cultivation. What works for medical may not be the best or most cost-effective solution for adult use.

As mentioned above, the industry's secrecy, intended to give producers a competitive advantage, is responsible for some of the challenges many are currently facing. In the last two decades of cultivation of medical cannabis, some pioneering work was done in facility design and operation. Clearly, there were breakthroughs, but were any shared with competitors? Not likely. This trend continues today. Many new innovations are created all the time and much good work out there is not setting standards because of the secrecy that persists in the industry. Over time, information sharing among grow associations would help break down some of these barriers.

Clearly, the grow industry is missing out considerably by not having building standards in place. Therefore, what kind of work is underway now to create them?

The American society of Agricultural and Biological engineers (ASABE) has taken notice of the vacuum that exists today and has partnered with ASHRAE to create a new guideline for indoor growing environments: ASABE X653 guideline "Heating, Ventilating, and Air Conditioning (HVAC) for Indoor Plant environments without sunlight."

The author of this book is a contributing member on the developing committee. This guideline is intended to provide clarity for engineers regarding the design and operation of isolated indoor plant environments, or in other words, warehouses that do not have windows and totally rely on high performance HVAC systems to control the environment.

Certainly, one reason engineers may be prone to make mistakes in this context is because grow rooms are so different from other indoor environments. For example, unlike most other types of facilities, grow room HVAC systems normally don't introduce any outdoor air. They are typically 100% recirculation with CO_2 added, to the tune of about three times the normal ambient concentration. This is just one of many examples, all of which contribute to significantly different requirements for the design of grow room HVAC systems that engineers who are unfamiliar with this space may not realize. The lack of any standards certainly does not help.

MISAPPLICATION OF TRADITIONAL EQUIPMENT

In many cases with new grow rooms, certain solutions have been used simply because they have worked before in other applications. As noted, the unique nature of the cannabis growing environment requires different approaches. Many of the solutions proposed in the recent past for grow rooms are simply not sufficient and deliver poor value for growers.

There are potentially many approaches to HVAC that could be applied to this space. However, some of them would be a misapplication of technology. One example is standard commercial air conditioners. As will be discussed in Chapter 8: HVAC System Types, these types of air conditioners have been a typical choice because they are inexpensive and are often used in similar large facilities. The setup is quite simple, and many engineers are familiar with how they work, so they feel comfortable applying them here.

But as we'll examine in more detail in Chapter 8, ordinary air conditioners are not necessarily well-suited to the grow space because they have some technical limitations that may cause them to be poor performers on the metrics that growers care about, such as control of humidity and ability to cool the indoor space when it is cold outside, not to mention energy efficiency and optimal room control.

The misapplication of technology has led to some growers spending a lot on new projects that involved equipment that doesn't work for what they need. The result is underperforming grows that cost even more because of reduced yield and higher operating expenses.

Fundamentally, the misapplication of technology is largely due to lack of knowledge and understanding of the products available on the part of many different stakeholders in the industry. This group includes engineers, but also contributing to this information vacuum are traditional HVAC suppliers and contractors.

On the side of manufacturers, one issue has been the lack of purpose-built HVAC equipment for grow rooms. Traditional large-scale manufacturers have been reluctant to invest R&D capital into producing a dedicated product for this marketplace for potentially many reasons: indecision over how to approach the design, questions about liability due to legal uncertainties, and uncertainty over whether the market opportunity was worth the required investment to make a new type of product. The cannabis market has had an arguably questionable trajectory until late 2018, with legalization in Canada, so the potential market size for HVAC manufacturers up until that point had been unclear.

> Few manufacturers offer purpose-built HVAC systems specifically for cannabis growing, due to reluctance to invest in R&D for a new market that was quite small until relatively recently.

For those who have entered the market, most are repurposing existing products designed for a different application. The solution does not necessarily need to be designed from scratch; some applications that bear similarity to grow rooms can provide a starting point. For example, indoor swimming pools have similar latent loads and operating conditions in terms of temperature and relative humidity levels. Accordingly, manufacturers of indoor pool dehumidifiers have been well-positioned to provide for the cannabis market, but only to a certain degree. There is still a requirement to further develop their product line specifically for grow rooms and not all have been willing to invest significantly in this option.

There are applications that are not as compatible with grow rooms. One example is data center air conditioning.

At face value, it would appear data centers are quite like grow rooms: they're both isolated indoor spaces with significant heat loads that originate from equipment that require active air conditioning year-round. For data centers, the heat comes from servers while, for grow rooms, it comes from lamps. But data centers have no need to dehumidify the air; in fact, most add humidity to help reduce static electricity. Meanwhile, grow rooms have a large humidity load due to plant transpiration and evaporation from the watering system. That makes a huge difference to the science and technology application. Therefore, the air conditioning equipment that works well in data centers does not usually apply well to grow rooms.

> Air conditioners for data centers are effective for cooling the air but are not usually designed to effectively remove moisture, because data centers typically want slightly humid air to control humidity in fine detail to protect the plants.

We understand the pain that growers are undergoing because of this misapplication and we want to help put an end to it. You can learn about possible equipment solutions in Chapter 8: HVAC System Types.

Related to misapplication of technology is poor implementation. For example, not all growers are familiar with the modern and high-tech building control systems of today. After all, they have never needed to use these systems before. Some growers are still sorting out their approach to building and equipment controls and not everybody understands how to properly implement them. This technology requires more involvement from equipment manufacturers and start-up contractors to solve. Building control systems, or specific equipment controls, may require software engineering to tailor their logic to the grower's needs.

The grower needs to take the lead in this situation because they are best suited to know exactly what is required. However, unfamiliarity with the technology leads to poor outcomes.

CONCLUSION

There are four main challenges facing growers who are attempting to scale up:

- A lack of experience across multiple domains.
- Market and regulatory pressures.
- Lack of standards.
- Misapplication of traditional equipment.

In short, the marketplace today faces many challenges that make scaling-up a tall task. By understanding these issues, we can move on to discussing some practical solutions throughout this book.

Further reading of the issues specifically discussed in this chapter can be found in Chapter 5: Navigating the Traditional Equipment Procurement Process and Chapter 8: HVAC System Types.

ECONOMICS OF GROWING

CHAPTER 03

The business of growing cannabis has changed significantly in a relatively short period of time, as has its scale, the economics, and the best practices of the fast-growing industry.

Now, as an ever-expanding legal market, growers have moved from basements and into boardrooms. Competition has increased significantly and that affects everything from the retail price per gram to whether growers will make certain decisions in their operations, such as investing in and taking advantage of more advanced technologies to improve quality, consistency, and efficiency which can have a direct impact on sales and profits.

You must understand the intent of a facility and its product before you can select an HVAC system. It's also important to understand the context of local regulations, the product branding and marketing, as well as the target audience. All of these factors are related in different ways to the HVAC system and will dictate how flexible, scalable, and precise the system needs to be to deliver expected performance and ROI.

The economics of growing vary a lot by jurisdiction.

Few markets and operator objectives are exactly the same, and therefore the challenges and objectives for one may be very different for another operator. For example, Hawthorne, the largest provider of products for the cannabis industry, has (as of the time of writing) over 6,000 items in their catalogue. Their goal is to accommodate the nuances and desires of growers large and small with exactly what they want, and therefore, the variety of options they provide is very large and continues to grow.

Some of this variation is due to different approaches by government regulators in each market. Another cause of different economics is the effect of local climate on growing, the type and size of facility, and the unique characteristics of the strain or type of cultivation the grower chooses, a topic discussed more in the next two chapters.

One constant in this economic shift of the industry is that everybody has essentially agreed that large-scale production is becoming a significant market driver, at least for the foreseeable future. When you think of the big players in cannabis, your mind probably turns to companies such as Canopy Growth. These companies have scaled-up significantly, both in Canada and in many countries around the world, and continue to do so. In a crowded field full of big companies, with large market capitalizations, the small producers are at risk of being marginalized or purchased if they do not operate efficiently. Years ago, scale didn't matter; you usually only had a few customers and could set prices to whatever made sense. Today, the market keeps expanding and there are supply shortages in most locales. Much like the plight of small farms in a world of agribusiness, small cannabis producers will increasingly have a hard time competing with high-volume growers, many of whom have significantly more resources to invest into research and operations.

In an industry like this, how do smaller growers manage? How can you gain market share and fend off the competition?

REGULATIONS SHAPE THE MARKET

The form that a cannabis market in North America takes largely depends on the regulatory environment which has a big impact on both the competitiveness of the marketplace as well as on how growers approach their cultivation, how they build out, and what technologies they may leverage.

The Oregon and Colorado markets offer a case study of comparison. Both states have legalized cannabis for medical applications as well as adult use, but their approaches to managing the market are quite different.

Oregon has largely taken a hands-off approach to its licensing process. This choice was a deliberate strategy to invite the industry into the state by providing a low barrier of entry.[12] There is no limit to the number of licenses a company or individual can acquire and there are no minimum residency requirements as in other states, such as Maine. Coupling that with the state's geography and climate, which are conducive to growing cannabis, and it's no surprise the market has taken off. There are over 1,100 licensed producers (as of writing) for adult use cannabis alone and applications keep coming in.[12]

As a result of this tremendous competition, the market has become saturated. According to a January 2019 report by the Oregon Liquor Control Commission, demand is approximately half of what the supply is, thus causing many producers to have a large surplus inventory of product.[12] The flooded market has been challenging for many businesses, as a *Guardian* headline from 2015 noted: "Two months after Oregon legalization, pot saturation sends profits up in smoke."[13]

Market saturation has predictable effects in any industry and cannabis is no different. The supply glut has significantly driven prices down for buyers, as the price per gram fell by about half, from more than $10 in October 2016 to under $5 by December of that same year, according to the Oregon Liquor Control Commission.[12]

Competing in a saturated market is challenging. Growers may be motivated to produce at high volumes in the hopes of catching a market share foothold by being recognized as a reliable source of product. But a flooded market makes this a risky proposition. If growers produce too much and are unable to sell their product, they will have effectively wasted money in producing an unsellable crop. Furthermore, an organization with unreliable cashflow could threaten local jobs.

The low market price for cannabis in some markets drives growers to reduce their costs as much as possible. Growers can leverage technologies such as LED lighting to reduce their operating expenses and make growing more economical.

LED significantly reduces electricity consumption as well as heat load on HVAC equipment, possibly by as much as 30%. Growers could also use more efficient building systems, such as a high-performing energy-recycling HVAC system. Due to the incentive to reduce operating costs, growers in these markets may benefit from making investments in these types of technologies.

The Oregon approach is quite different from that of Colorado, as the Oregon Liquor Control Commission observed in its report: "Oregon's current market dynamic of supply exceeding demand strongly contrasts with Colorado, where there are more robust supply-side constraints enforced as part of licensure. Although Colorado does not have a hard cap on the numbers of licenses, regulators strictly enforce producer canopy allotments by forcing individual producers down in allotted canopy if they cannot demonstrate sufficient market for the amount of marijuana they produce."[12]

Colorado has experienced a more balanced market, largely due to its regulatory approach. Consumer prices have recently trended downward in that state as well, simply as a function of increased production.[14]

Results in Canada have been similar to that of any new market, in that it is experiencing a major supply shortage. New cannabis markets typically need some time to scale up and produce enough volume to meet consumer demand and allow growers to work out some kinks in their operations. This is not necessarily related to regulations; however, Canada's approach may be slowing down growers' ability to start up. They must have two grows assessed in order to receive a production permit. Additionally, rules were implemented in mid-2019 that require growers to have a fully built site before they can apply for a permit. This was intended to reduce the government backlog of hundreds of pending permits for facilities that would not have been built for some time. Small producers face some risk because they have uncertainty going into construction regarding their permit. Such uncertainty may make it harder to raise capital and could slow some businesses down in their journey to building.

> Local regulations are important because they may hold great sway over business direction. For example, certain regulations might influence the selection of unitary HVAC solutions.

In areas with regulations such as in Canada, growers will find themselves preferring to build small first phases to get their necessary permits and then add onto the structures in the medium- to long-term, after they have approvals and get a crop going. This requires some thought in how you will design a facility that is scalable in nature and function.

Certain geographies change the game for growing, too.

A grower can choose to host their crop in different kinds of facilities, and the type that is most desirable depends largely on the grower's location. For example, a greenhouse without artificial light can work in California, but a fully enclosed warehouse without sunlight would be better in northern latitudes. **For more discussion, see Chapter 4: Navigating the Building Design Process.**

BUILDING A BRAND

In the highly competitive cannabis market, one of the key ways for companies to attract customers is to build a strong brand identity for themselves through both marketing initiatives as well as with the product itself.

Branding poses a unique challenge in this industry, as some regulatory environments impose significant limits on what kind of marketing is allowed. Mass advertising is difficult, as Google (as of this writing) does not permit cannabis ads on any of its platforms, even in legal markets. Other major digital advertising networks impose restrictions, as does legacy media, most of whom are ambivalent towards cannabis companies. Radio and TV advertising in most states may or may not be allowed, often depending on the likelihood of a large number of minors possibly seeing the content. In the U.S., cannabis marketing via the USPS is not permitted, at least on paper. In fact, regulations may restrict or even ban any mass communications regarding cannabis products, out of fear of inadvertently appealing to minors.

This is the case in Canada, where the government has forbidden most kinds of marketing for cannabis. The strict rules have

LED to some unusual results as even industry news sites have put up an age verification wall to make sure no one under the age of 19 can see information about cannabis.

With advertising posing some significant challenges, companies are limited in what they can say about their products to entice potential customers. Companies are generally allowed to provide information about the characteristics of their product. For adult use cannabis, this can include mentioning the THC content, the aroma it produces when smoked, as well as other attributes that buyers might like to know. Product descriptions for certain strains closely resemble what you might find written about certain types of wines or craft beers.

For medical cannabis, companies generally provide factual highlights about the benefits of a particular strain and what purposes it could serve. Users in the medical segment are generally interested in how the product will help them manage pain or specific symptoms. They are typically (but not necessarily) looking for products that have high CBD concentrations, as that chemical is most frequently associated with medicinal benefits. (That said, THC has some medical applications, too; for example, with anti-inflammation or for sleep aid.) Usually, they're going for indica strains or a hybrid.

With the wide range in strains and possible uses for cannabis, there is a need for a high level of control and flexible conditions in the cultivation of product. An efficient and high performing HVAC system plays a critical role in this process.

This differentiation also exists in the adult use market, where consumers may be interested in a wide variety of strains, depending on the desired effect. They want to know how pleasurable the cannabis will be to use and what kind of outcome it will produce; for example, whether it will be relaxing or provide a social boost. Many factors influence what they will buy, such as the time of day they are planning to consume it.

There are many different types of adult use buyers, all of whom must be catered to in different ways. The target markets are changing and becoming more varied, too. For example, many professional white-collar people are now interested in trying cannabis. They may be looking for a product that can soothe their stressors but are also concerned about being seen as "stoners." Therefore, the company selling the product should avoid that stereotype. Professionals are an example of how method of consumption can change depending on demographic; they may be more likely to try edibles or prefer to vape, instead of smoke.

Different demographics may choose to consume cannabis in different ways. Companies need to know their target market so they can produce the kind of product their customers are seeking.

Parents, young and old, are another emerging market segment. As cannabis continues to be normalized, some parents are turning to it as a grown-up pleasure after their kids have been put to bed or sent to summer camp. One mother told Today's Parent that they even prefer cannabis to alcohol, as they thought it was easier to control their consumption and avoid overindulging, in case their child needed attention.[15]

In fact, about 82% of 800 cannabis users in legal U.S. states who were surveyed in 2016 by Miner and Co. Studio said they preferred cannabis to other substances such as alcohol. The survey found the average age of cannabis consumers was 30 and most were male: 65% compared to 35%.[16]

The male tilt of cannabis users has been observed elsewhere. The Q1 2019 National Cannabis Survey, by Statistics Canada, found that 22% of Canadian males reported using cannabis while that figure was 13% for females.[17] Overall, users tended to be younger. The survey said 30% of people aged 15–24 years old said they used cannabis, while 16% of those aged 25 and older reported having used it.[17]

Younger users may have different tastes than those trending older. Established older users will probably be more accustomed to the lower THC concentrations that were typical of the past, whereas younger users will be quite familiar with the elevated THC levels that have become so ubiquitous in recent years. The producer will want to determine who their target markets are and then provide products that cater to them.

For example, Aphria Inc., a large Canadian producer, has created different brands that are tailored to differing market segments, which were developed after a year of research, the company's investor presentation says.[18]

In the "enthusiast" category, they offer the value-brand Good Supply, which is described on their website: "It grows out of the earth and we pass it along. We know it's the quality of the product that matters. And since we like to sit back and let it do its thing, we just get the bud to you for what we think is a good price. No bullshit." It's no-frills pot. Meanwhile, "passive risk takers" are targeted by Riff, the middle-of-the-road-priced brand. Aphria describes this brand as "for the discerning cannabis consumer with an eye for the little things." The Solei brand, pitched as a "sustainable sun-grown product" is geared towards relaxers and novices. Broken Coast is for connoisseurs, with its "keen eye for quality" and small-batch, hand-trimmed harvests from single-strain rooms.

As highlighted by these brand descriptions, different growing conditions may be used to tailor a product to its intended audience.

In locales where regulations restrict branding on packaging, being recognized by your target market depends entirely on producing good strains that people will want and ask for, again and again. Similar to tobacco products, some regulatory set-ups do not permit any sort of brand information on packages other than the company name and the strain.

This leaves it almost entirely to the grower to craft a product that people will come to know independent of the packaging. While cannabis has a lot in common with craft beer, the similarity somewhat ends here. Craft brewers have long relied on unique and eye-catching can designs to get people excited about their brew as they walk past the cooler. With cannabis, you often can't do that. Packaging can be quite limited, and some jurisdictions even limit what can actually be displayed in a store. Instead, the focus here is mostly on the strain itself rather than its packaging.

You can get customers' attention by producing a strain that:

- consistently delivers what the customer is looking for: either a desirable CBD or THC level, a good smell and flavor, a specific kind of terpene, a low price, and so on;
- is known to consistently offer a premium experience; and
- is readily available (grown at-scale, quickly, and efficiently.)

When the grower provides a strain that offers these key attributes, customers will be looking for it in their local cannabis store. Price isn't necessarily a deal breaker; for example, if you are catering to a connoisseur-type audience, they may not mind paying top-dollar if it gets them good value. Higher price points may carry certain benefits that the grower can provide, such as certified lab testing, organic cultivation, or even assurance that the strain is grown only in small batches.

Many other companies have found success in offering consistent and quality products. Starbucks, McDonald's, and Coca-Cola are great examples. Despite many thousands of locations, Starbucks and McDonald's use very tight controls to ensure their products at each location follow certain standards to guarantee an almost identical experience for every customer, every time. They have become very well known for their offerings, which are widely available at nearly all their stores.

Coca-Cola, which pioneered the concept of buying bottled soft drinks to take home, is also universally known for their diverse lineup of refreshing beverages that were all built on the same principle of enjoying the moment with one of their drinks in hand. For over 100 years, Coca-Cola has remained relevant mainly because they have consistently offered their signature Coke product, always to the same high standard of quality. In fact, the company very nearly hit an iceberg when they tried changing to the New Coke formula in the 1980s. Even though many people reported they preferred the new formula's taste, people were not happy with the change overall. Ensuing consumer backlash convinced the company to change course and re-introduce the original Coke while stopping production of the new formulation.[19]

The "New Coke debacle" has since become a case study in the value of a product for brands and why you should never mess with success. Growers can apply these lessons to the production and sale of their strains.

Although regulations can be restrictive, they generally allow the producer to describe their strains and offer their take on how they work best.

Descriptions are generally short and similar to what you'd find in a winery. For example, here is how Aurora describes their San Rafael '71 Pink Kush indica strain: "Cancel any plans and chill like a champ. Pink Kush is a great strain for unwinding — especially at night. Dark Green and purple in color, this indica balances notes of pine and lemon." It further says the strain pairs well with "Burning and crashing, your vinyl collection (and/or) a comfortable pillow."

It is clear from this description how a different strain can appeal to specific audiences, depending on what they are looking for. In their description, Aurora has also set an expectation for the customer that the product will be consistent in quality and delivery of outcome. Therefore, a controlled grow is very important.

CROP QUALITY MATTERS

If you want to know why the quality and consistency of your grow matters, you only need to ask The Supreme Cannabis Company. As noted in their investor presentation: "Eighty-five per cent of cannabis enthusiasts will not purchase products that have sub-par scent. Sixty-three per cent of cannabis enthusiasts will reject product that does not pass their visual inspection."[20]

Buyers do not want a product that smells unpleasant. They are also wary of mold or other contaminants on their bud. They expect a good product and the grower must provide that or lose profit as a consequence.

The Supreme Cannabis Company has noted the so-called entourage effect as a key influencer of what kind of experience a strain will provide. The effect is derived from the confluence of hundreds of different cannabinoids, terpenes, and other chemicals found in cannabis.[20] Recently, more growers have recognized the critical role that terpenes play in cannabis effect, which is heavily influenced by the way you grow your crop.

There are some variables at play, however. For example, if you are growing for extraction, then you don't need to control for smell as it will not be an issue for the end product. Recognize that the final product and expected outcomes may be different for your target markets and that may dictate different approaches and metrics for crop quality.

Smoking remains the #1 way to consume cannabis, as it is cheap, simple, and provides quick action. According to Deloitte, about 42% of the market prefers to use joints. There is some variance among method of consumption depending on frequency. Daily users tend to prefer joints, whereas those who use only weekly, lean slightly more towards bongs. Those who use monthly are partial to vaporizers.[21]

CONCLUSION

The economics of growing cannabis has changed somewhat in the past few years as the industry has legalized, thus requiring greater scale in the way growers operate. While the black market typically involved selling to a smaller community of buyers, growers today are selling to the mass market. This is a game changer.

There are some challenges in selling to the mass market. For one, most jurisdictions place significant restrictions on marketing and advertising that makes it very challenging to get attention around your product. For example, packaging is generally plain, with only the strain, brand, and details on its content. The way to get people interested is to produce a high-quality strain that appeals specifically to your target market.

There's a variety of market segments in cannabis today, many of whom have slightly differing tastes. Strains or even entire brands can be developed to cater to their wants. One of the key differentiators for cannabis products is their perceived quality and consistency, as well as their concentration of certain desirable chemicals, such as terpenes, that are influenced heavily by growing conditions. These considerations point to the importance of a precision HVAC system for all aspects of business success in this sector.

NAVIGATING THE BUILDING DESIGN PROCESS

CHAPTER 04

Central to the economics of any cannabis-growing operation is the environment in which it takes place. After all, the type of facility you grow in will influence everything else, from the type of lighting used to whether you will need an HVAC system, what type, plus all other critical building systems.

There is considerable variety in the types of facilities being used to grow cannabis. From pure greenhouse to mixed light to fully enclosed, these facilities may be new construction, retrofit, or simply a conversion from some other less lucrative crop. Some of these choices are driven by geography and climate, others by capital budget, speed to market, or even licensing requirements.

Whatever the circumstance, each facility type and location is somewhat unique as far as creating the ideal growing environment.

Given a lack of building standards in place among the engineering community, and a general expertise deficit about the best solutions, a great deal of confusion persists in the decision-making process around building design.

There is no cookie-cutter solution for the perfect facility for every grower, and the right decision is not always clear. Designing and implementing the right solution can often take more time and careful consideration than many growers are currently providing. Yet, making the right call will seriously affect the bottom line with regard to crop quality, volume, and consistency, not to mention capital costs, energy consumption, and ongoing maintenance costs – which can be a significant percentage of total operating costs.

How big do you want to go? How fast can you scale? How much capital do you have access to? Do your licensing requirements restrict the pace of your growth? What size and how many rooms do you want? There are many possible answers to these critical questions that will drive your facility size and type and, in turn, your HVAC requirements.

While size has its benefits, there are also good reasons to start small and build up as an alternative strategy. Given certain license requirements in some areas, it may be faster and more efficient to start out with a smaller facility and expand over time.

Besides the size of the facility, there's also the critical issue of what type of facility you want. Greenhouse or warehouse? Mixed-light, or no sunlight? Should it be a new purpose-built structure, or will you convert an existing facility for production?

The decision here will echo throughout every harvest you produce in the facility, so you must consider all of the relevant factors.

WHAT TYPE OF FACILITY TO CHOOSE?

There are four main types of operations that can be deployed to grow cannabis at commercial scale in North America:

1. **No enclosure (outdoor grow).**
2. **Greenhouse without artificial lighting.**
3. **Mixed-light greenhouse.**
4. **Warehouse without sunlight.**

A key determiner on the viability of these four types of facility is geographic location.

HOW GEOGRAPHY AFFECTS GROWING

One major factor that will greatly affect the economics of growing, including the type of facility you use, is your geographical location. Different climates influence capital and operating costs, as well as the viability of commercial grows. Local climate conditions necessitate different solutions than what is standard somewhere else. Because a major challenge facing the grow industry today is misapplication of technology, understanding the impact of geography will go a long way toward avoiding mistakes or inefficiencies.

Cannabis is also known as weed, for good reason. The plant grows like a weed and, as such, has been known to flourish in a wide variety of geographies and climates. Since humans began cultivating cannabis in Asia millennia ago, it spread over time to most of the globe as a result of exploration and colonization. Genetic engineering by humans and natural mutation on the part of the plant has led to the creation of countless cannabis strains, some of which do better in certain conditions specific to a particular geography. For example, some strains do well outdoors and can tolerate varying conditions natural to that environment, while others require care inside, under more strictly-controlled conditions. Indica strains generally cope well with colder northern climates, while sativa is well-adapted to warmer zones.

With the industry rapidly expanding across the whole continent, growers are looking for more options than down south. Many facilities are being built further north, in Ontario or Quebec, for example. But the type of facility that worked in California will not necessarily be ideal for a northern climate.

The most obvious way geography affects growing is through local climate. The U.S. has the most diverse climate from coast to coast of any country on the globe. Each of these climates has its own unique attributes that will dramatically affect the way you need to approach cannabis cultivation. These differences may allow some strains to be grown outside, while in other areas you may need to use greenhouses. Elsewhere, you will require a fully enclosed indoor environment to provide the right conditions for growth.

Some variables of climate zones:

- Dew point (absolute humidity) influences relative humidity and the risk of mold on plants. Humidity will also influence vapor pressure differential, a major influencer on growth.
- Average temperatures are a critical issue for many strains. Sativa plants typically need the warmest temperatures, while indica, with its dense leaves, can handle cooler temperatures. Temperatures that are too cool will limit growth, while high temperatures will cause damaging heat stress, stunting the crop and creating foxtails.
- Rainfall: some areas are wetter than others.
- Risk of natural disasters like tornadoes or hurricanes that could destroy a crop are also a consideration.

Other factors of geography to consider:

- Elevation influences temperature and humidity. For every thousand meters added in elevation, the temperature will be about 6.5°C lower. Additionally, higher elevations are drier, and the air is thinner, meaning less CO_2 is available.
- Photoperiod: length of day varies drastically depending on locale and season. In the south,

photoperiod can be more consistent throughout the year, while it will fluctuate more in the north and be shorter during winter.

- Winds, especially high-speed winds, can affect transpiration.

NO ENCLOSURE

One could argue growing cannabis outside is the most authentic way possible. After all, the adult use black market in North America was supplied by outdoor grow-ops in Mexico during the early half of the 20th century.[3,9]

Likely, outdoor is also the cheapest way to grow cannabis, given no electricity is needed to run lights or HVAC. There would be some costs associated with the watering system, staff payroll, plus pesticides and herbicides.

Even given that, the overall operating expenses of an outdoor grow could be lower. Jeannette VanderMarel, co-CEO of 48 North Cannabis, told Canadian Business that the cost of growing outdoors is estimated at 25 cents per gram, compared to 90 to 100 cents per gram for greenhouse grows and about two dollars for indoor, no-sunlight crops.[22]

Besides lower expenses, growing outdoors may carry some other benefits. Some evidence suggests that outdoor crops can be larger than comparable plants grown indoors.[23] Possibly, outdoor plants have more space to stretch their roots and grow their leaves, allowing them to absorb more sunlight and grow even more over the course of their life through to harvest.[24]

However, there are some cons as well. The grower has no control over their crop. They cannot adjust CO_2 levels (which happens to be a limiting factor for plant growth) and have no say over how much sunlight the plants get. They may water the plants, but the skies may decide to add even more water. Watering during hot and dry summer days may be challenging as water could evaporate before the plants can absorb it. There is no control over relative humidity, and as a result, plants can get moldy or become stunted. They may also take on parasites, making pesticides a requirement for outdoor operations, which is risky for the end-user of the product. Storms and natural disasters could destroy the crop very easily. In most parts of North America, it is only possible to grow outdoors for part of the year before the cold season sets in. Given the lack of control, the grow cycles also take more time to go through.

As a result of all these issues, the grower has a significant liability because there is little they can do to protect their crop from all of these threats. In addition, the crop is likely to be inconsistent. There are challenges in maintaining a consistent year-round supply given the seasonal nature of outdoor growing.

As quality and consistency are the main differentiators for cannabis products, the outdoor proposition may not be viable for most growers. For a medical product, with its many regulatory demands and stringent requirements, outdoor growing is likely not viable. In addition, seasonal growing requires seasonal workers, which may pose additional business management challenges.

Usually, growing outside has been restricted to the milder climates typically found in the southern U.S., like California or Florida. Outdoor growing also happens in Oregon, British Columbia, and Southern Ontario.

That said, some growers are experimenting more with outdoor grows around the continent, even in Canada. WeedMD Inc. and Canopy are some of the companies who are looking closely at outdoor commercial grows. In 2019, Canopy started a pilot project to conduct a 160-acre-sized grow in northern Saskatchewan.[25] Bruce Linton, while serving as co-CEO of Canopy Growth, told *BNN Bloomberg* that growing outdoors would likely not become a sustainable long-term business strategy for Canopy, given quality concerns, but suggested outdoor crops could be usable for extraction. "Anything grown outdoors will not be of bud quality," he told the news network in an interview.[26]

Growing for extraction in an outdoor setting may even be ideal. VanderMarel of 48 North Cannabis told *Postmedia* that plants grown outdoors tend to produce more terpenes due to their exposure to the elements. These terpenes are highly valuable for producing cannabis extracts.[24]

GREENHOUSE WITHOUT ARTIFICIAL LIGHTING

Basic greenhouses were one of the first methods commercial growers explored when cannabis became legal. Faced with the challenges of growing outdoors, greenhouses were seen as a compromise. You can harness the power of the sun to significantly reduce operating costs, but also protect your crop from some of the biggest risks of outdoor grows. Greenhouses were originally used for medical grows and some have been used for more recent adult use operations as well.

Greenhouses without artificial lighting are only viable in areas where sunlight remains relatively stable throughout the year. There may be no control over the light, in which case the crop will be exposed to whatever the sky has on offer for the entire day. Curtains or covers could also be used to block out any light beyond what is needed for the crop at its current stage of the grow cycle. The electricity savings of using the sun are significant, given that the Northwest Power and Conservation Council claims that about 80% of electricity used in growing cannabis is attributable directly and indirectly to the lighting.[11]

Greenhouses are typically quick and easy to acquire and operate. Many of the greenhouses in operation today actually started their lives hosting very different kinds of crop, such as tomatoes or strawberries. They were then purchased by cannabis companies who converted them to their own requirements. The cost of this conversion is relatively low and can make the start-up phase a little simpler.

Constructing a new greenhouse, especially without artificial lighting, may also be cheaper than a warehouse by a significant degree. There is no requirement to install a light array, nor is there a need for an HVAC system to be in place. In fact, it would usually not be advisable to install an HVAC system in a greenhouse as the cost of operating it would likely be impractical, especially in northern climates, because windows do not retain heat well. Geography is such a key factor in choosing certain types of facilities. Therefore, your only control of interior heat and humidity is opening windows, which may not be precise enough for the plant's needs: it will never be cooler inside than it is outside. As well, open windows may invite pests such as insects or birds, which can damage the crops.

Despite savings on lighting and HVAC, a greenhouse could yet be more costly, depending on the scale. For a large operation, it may be smarter to build a warehouse because, in order to capture sufficient sunlight, a greenhouse can only be one story tall. Thus, the amount of land the greenhouse uses would be proportional to the desired output. Larger quantities of crop would require a larger plot of land. Conversely, a warehouse can be multiple stories tall. Since the greatest cost to a new building is in constructing the first floor, it may be cheaper to build a multi-story enclosed structure that uses less land rather than a big greenhouse that spans a vast space. For that reason, it follows that warehouses may be preferable for very large grows.

In the right geographic location, greenhouses without artificial lighting could be a very viable method of production. While planning an investment in growing cannabis, it's important to perform due diligence and consider all the factors. If the lack of control and risk of lower crop quality/consistency are acceptable trade-offs in exchange for reduced capital and operating costs, then this method may be feasible.

MIXED-LIGHT GREENHOUSE

These are a step up from the converted tomato greenhouses of the past. Many mixed-light greenhouses are purpose-built for growing cannabis and incorporate the latest technologies conducive to creating ideal conditions.

Mixed-light facilities are still significantly limited by numerous factors, but, thanks to the addition of lamps, lack of light isn't one of them.

Growing in the north in a greenhouse is now possible with a mixed-light facility. Due to long and grey winters, sunlight in some of the northern U.S. and most of Canada can be a hard-to-come-by commodity, especially for the large number of exposed hours that plants require to grow to their fullest. With the addition of artificial lighting, the grower can save some electricity by using the sun when it is available and then simply turn on their lamps when natural light is insufficient. Lights are often either on/off, although it is possible to modify their intensity to run when there is some sunlight, but not quite enough.

Again, greenhouses can often be relatively inexpensive to construct. However, the gap narrows with mixed light facilities because of the need to add lights and run them. Assuming a 100,000 sq. ft. greenhouse, with lights costing $56 per square foot to install, the cost alone is $5.6 million. Running them would add more expense due to the cost of electricity. If the greenhouse was located north (for example, in Canada), the sunlight would likely be insufficient during the winter. Therefore, supplemental lighting may be needed for roughly half of the year. The lights would then be on for about 25% of the total hours within that period of half the year that lights may be called for, or 1,095 hours. If HPS lights use 1kW per 20 square feet, then the cost is about $491,381.25 for the year. (Lights using 5,475 MWh per year, at a rate of $89.75 per MWh.) As a result, the majority of electricity savings for lighting will be during the summer, unless the facility is located in the right geographic area.

Another issue is heat. While mixed-light facilities make it possible to grow further north, the winters there are very cold. While the lights, especially if high-intensity discharge, will add some heat into the space, that will only be of benefit during lights-on mode. Even then, their heat load may not be sufficient because glass loses heat to the outside very quickly. Therefore, the application of a heating system will be required.

Another factor to consider is the effect of climate change over the coming decades. Changes in many areas around the globe are expected to cause more frequent seasonal extremes that could reduce the operation of a greenhouse which is more exposed to the elements. For example, warmer-than-average summers, with more frequent heat waves, could lead to extreme heat inside the greenhouse that could damage or destroy the crop. Before selecting a greenhouse facility, some prudent local climate modeling could determine how to prepare for future changes.

While mixed-light facilities are worth considering, the grower needs to carefully model the costs to determine if this method would offer better ROI than a fully enclosed warehouse.

WAREHOUSE WITHOUT SUNLIGHT

The fully enclosed indoor environment allows the grower to be like Mother Nature. All the normal limiting factors of plant growth — light levels, CO_2 levels, water, temperature, and humidity — are fully under the control of the grow master with the right equipment and controls.

While a greenhouse is a step up from growing outside, it is very different from the tightly controlled environment that is only possible with a warehouse-type space. Within a warehouse, the degree of control over almost all factors is practically unlimited. Plant yield and consistency can be maximized, while loss due to disease and stunting can be minimized.

It's true that certain costs are higher with a warehouse. The building itself is more expensive to construct, and maintenance and operating costs may be higher. However, labor costs may be lower because more operations can be automated and generally run more efficiently.

Assuming a floor space of 100,000 square feet, at an increased cost of $15 per square foot, the difference in capital cost of a fully enclosed building is $1.5 million. Lighting is $56 per square foot, an expense that exists regardless of mixed light or warehouse. A generally recognized budget value for mechanical equipment (heating, cooling, dehumidification, and ventilation) is $75 per square foot, which adds another $7.5 million to the cost.

The difference in total capital cost for this warehouse grow is about $9.0 million.

Factors such as light, humidity, and the presence of pesticides can greatly affect the quality of the cannabis crop. The first two cannot be controlled effectively inside a greenhouse and the latter becomes a necessity.

Cannabis requires specific humidity levels that vary depending on the type of plant and its stage in the growing cycle. If there is too much humidity, the crop could develop mold, mildew, or viral infections. If there's too little, cannabis will slow its own growth as it enters drought-resistant mode to conserve energy. Humidity also plays a critical role in yield. Cannabis cannot efficiently transpire if it is too humid, which will slow growth. The right dehumidification equipment will increase yield, allowing for more money-making potential.

Being able to control all environmental factors, including intensity of light, can also enable faster grow cycles and therefore more yield per square foot. Additionally, engineering of the plant to improve certain characteristics, like THC content, is more practical in this setting.

There are some costs associated with this greater degree of control. Aggregate data from our fleet of installed units shows an annualized compressor runtime average of about 56%, so this example facility should expect to spend roughly $493,000 annually, producing some 7.9 million refrigeration ton-hours.

In this controlled environment, the grower will have a competitive edge by minimizing product loss while maximizing quality and productivity. Even a few percent increase in yield can have a huge impact on a facility's revenue projections, and it's not uncommon to hear growers gleefully informing us of 20+% increases versus legacy technologies.

Being able to produce higher quality crop more efficiently will be a differentiator for the grower, both to customers and investors. And with many facilities looking for exclusivity agreements, the capacity to produce quickly and consistently can be a deal maker or a deal breaker.

Besides plant comfort, warehouses can also improve human productivity. One example is facility size. Since greenhouses can only be one story tall, they tend to have significant girth. A warehouse could shift its area more towards height, which makes traveling around the building quicker. As employees spend less time moving around, productivity could increase. How much more comfortable would they be working in a controlled environment rather than a hot, humid greenhouse? How many fewer breaks will they need to take because of the environmental difference? These questions are difficult to answer with a direct dollar value but deserve some weight.

Fully enclosed warehouses are a favorable solution when the grower wants total control or is in a location where a greenhouse would not be economical. Warehouses can be used to grow anything, including and especially medical-grade product. With the adult-use cannabis market becoming highly competitive, the quality and consistency that warehouse grows offer can be the foundation for a brand.

ALL THINGS CONSIDERED

This overview of the four main types of facilities that can be used to grow cannabis at commercial scale in North America presents some of the pros and cons of each choice. Again, none of these facilities is necessarily better than the other. They have different strengths and weaknesses and the choice should be a business decision based on what will provide better ROI for the grower. For example, the increased costs of building and operating an indoor environment without sunlight may be worthwhile if the grower can improve their crop's yield and quality, while minimizing loss due to spoilage. Since these improvements may lead to more revenue, the investment may be worthwhile. This decision can only be settled after a careful examination of all the factors.

NEW OR RETROFIT?

The number of purpose-built cannabis facilities being constructed has been on the rise recently. Generally, it's preferable to use a facility designed specifically with cannabis production in mind; however, the cost is certainly higher. In the past, and still today, converting existing facilities like warehouses or greenhouses to cannabis production is popular and often cost-effective.

Greenhouses are plentiful across North America. It's very cheap to buy an old indoor tomato farm and convert it to grow cannabis instead. And there is no shortage of old and fairly large warehouses in rural and industrial settings where they can be purchased relatively easily and inexpensively.

However, when a warehouse is purchased, often significant interior work must be done to bring it up to requirements. Usually the grower will want to knock out some walls and rip out any structure or fixtures that are surplus to needs. Electrical systems for lighting and HVAC often need upgrading and windows may need to be covered or removed.

Usually the aim will be to create as large and continuous a space as possible, which can then be subdivided into multiple rooms for separated production. This gives the grower the option to produce a variety of plant strains often separated into different rooms by grow stage. Another advantage of smaller, separate rooms is to reduce the risks of total crop contamination, should an infestation of some sort arise.

An effective way to subdivide rooms in new or retrofitted buildings is to use structural steel insulated panels (SIPs), which are also used to construct walk-in freezers in the cold storage industry. These affordable and modular construction materials are airtight and simple to install. They are fabricated offsite in pieces and trucked to the site to be fastened together to create rooms. The build-time is very quick and does not introduce many contaminants; for example, there is no drywall dust.

SIPs are fully washable, allowing the grower to clear a room after a cycle has been completed and hose them down before bringing in another grow, which more easily keeps a facility sanitized and reduces the risk of contamination. They also have a good insulation value, which improves efficiency.

> To protect against cross contamination, it's important to do a full washdown in between every grow cycle, including the room structure (such as floors and walls), as well as ducts and the HVAC unit. Design elements that enable easy cleaning are beneficial; for example, using fabric ducts means you can easily take them down for laundering.

Retrofitting is a very attractive method to start production because it can be done very quickly compared to building a new facility. Renovations may need less involvement from architects and professional engineers. The land zoning may even already allow for cannabis production, depending on the municipality.

The downside is that you are shoehorning into a building that wasn't designed to grow cannabis at commercial scale. You will likely encounter challenges that require costly solutions. For example, electrical systems may need significant upgrades to supply the power-intensive lighting. Additionally, the HVAC system in place would likely not be sufficient, requiring upgrading. Even something as simple as not having the right size doors in the right locations for the space could pose problems for the grower.

Retrofitted facilities may face challenges in accommodating the addition of large HVAC equipment and air flow capacity redesign. Roof load weight restrictions, access halls, and finding the right sized physical location for equipment can often present problems. The capacities required are often 4 to 8 times greater than traditional building loads, thus requiring larger equipment. Often, these retrofitted facilities do not have enough space for the equipment. A grower interested in a retrofit structure should consider this factor in the onset of the project and should get all parties involved sooner rather than later to head off such issues.

You must account for insufficiencies with the building. For example, can the ceiling/roof handle the increased humidity of the space? It may need to be upgraded or provided increased coverage by the HVAC system.

Building new allows you to avoid these issues entirely because they can all be accounted for in the design. The entire structure can be highly customized and made more conducive towards excellent growing conditions.

Of course, building new is a more expensive proposition. Not only does the facility have to be designed, it must be constructed. If the grower holds land where a building already exists, demolition is required. The grower must wait for the municipality to grant a building permit on top of re-zoning, if applicable, and it takes time to build the structure. This process adds time to the project, and time is money.

Greenhouses are fairly inexpensive to construct while warehouses can be quite expensive. As noted earlier, some economies of scale can be found with warehouses if they have multiple stories, as opposed to a large single-story greenhouse.

INCORPORATING REDUNDANCY, SCALABILITY

You can design your facility through a variety of means to reduce the risk of losing large amounts of crop. Certainly, some key measures include the choice of building material (SIP, as noted), the quality of the HVAC system (and its air filters), as well as the degree to which the environment is exposed to the outdoors. Another way you can reduce risk is by building redundancy into the building itself.

Consider limiting the total canopy area per room to limit your exposure if one of the rooms is contaminated. Sealing the rooms with airtight building materials and separated HVAC systems are also helpful and could potentially reduce your insurance premiums as well.

Subdividing the facility into multiple rooms is a standard practice in the industry because the grower can then rotate crops and put plants in a specific room depending on the grow cycle. Managing the environment of these different rooms usually requires independent HVAC systems.

Typically, the room set-up is as follows:

- **Mother room:** Commercial cannabis plants typically originate from a "mother" plant, rather than seeds. This enables their growth to remain true to a specific strain and eliminate mutations. A mother plant, according to Aurora Cannabis, is "a healthy, adult, female cannabis plant from which clones can be created using cuttings."[27] The grower selects mother plants based on the characteristics they have, such as an ideal level of THC or CBD or for being particularly resilient. Mother plants live for a long time and are often used for months or years. Branches of the mother plants are cut to re-plant and "clone" the mother. This is a process known as vegetative propagation. (Alternatively, there is tissue culture propagation, where a small piece of tissue is taken from plants and used to clone in a sterile laboratory. This method allows for genetic manipulation of the strain.)[28] Conditions are approximately 78–80°F and 60% RH.

- **Cloning Room:** The cuts removed from mother plants are transplanted into soil where they are allowed to grow under continuous light, high (up to 80%) humidity, and a consistent temperature (usually 75–85°F). The high temperature and humidity in this space makes HVAC particularly challenging. Cuttings can take a week, or up to a month, to take root.[28]
- **Vegetative (veg) Room:** The clones, now maturing, are potted and moved here where they spend 2 to 8 weeks growing quickly. Like a teenaged human, these maturing plants need large amounts of energy, requiring constant exposure to light to photosynthesize. Between 12 to 18 hours of light is required, on the lower end if using sunlight and closer to 18 hours if using artificial light. Roots are constantly stretching and absorbing water. The plant transpires in this stage, so the room must have good vapor pressure differential controls with enough airflow to slightly bristle the leaves. Due to evaporative cooling off the leaves, temperatures are kept higher, usually 71° to 82°F during lights-on. RH starts near 70%, shifting down over time, usually by 5% per week. The grower manipulates the light cycle to either keep plants in vegetation longer, thus allowing them to grow more, or to enter the next stage. Providing 12 hours of continuous darkness will mimic the fall

season to the plants, thus sending them into the next stage.

- Lighting requirements are different for vegetation and a wide variety of types can be used. Plants in vegetation state appear to thrive under blue-spectrum light; metal-halide lamps are typically used here because they lean towards blue wavelengths. Also applicable for vegetation rooms are wideband LED, T5 fluorescent, and light-emitting plasma. Traditionally, high-pressure sodium vapor bulbs are not used here due to their preference to yellow and red light output, but some growers have reported success using them for vegetation.
- **Flowering Room:** When the plant has developed sufficiently, it is ready for flowering. Typically, plants are moved into the flowering room where they are kept in the dark for 12 uninterrupted hours, causing them to enter the flowering stage. Then they are given 12 hours of light on, 12 hours off. The plants produce buds at this stage, which can last 6–8 weeks. Humidity is kept low to prevent mold on the bud, generally starting higher and dropping as low as 40% RH towards the end of the cycle. Temperature is typically between 68° and 79°F, which also tends to be reduced as the plant matures.

- **Drying Room:** When the grower is satisfied, the product can be harvested and processed according to application. If processing is done on-site, there will be drying rooms, curing rooms, etc. The temperature, humidity, and volume of air flow can vary considerably depending on the quantity of product and desired rate of drying.

Many smaller rooms can allow for a wider variety of crop strains, stages of growth, and customized conditions than a few larger rooms.

HVAC can be designed in a scalable way around these smaller rooms. For example, you can use individual, unitary units to serve each individual room according to its specific needs. This setup enables the use of many smaller units rather than one large system. For increased redundancy, more than one unit can serve the same grow room, minimizing the potential risks associated with an equipment failure.

It's advisable for the grower to leave some flexibility for future expansion in their design as their business grows. From a business perspective, scalable design is highly beneficial.

Certain regulatory environments may require a grower to complete multiple harvests before they can receive a production permit. As a result, the grower may choose to limit their initial capital exposure by building a small first phase to satisfy this requirement. After the permit is approved, the facility can be built out over time to accommodate more canopy area. Choosing scalable designs and equipment, such as unitary HVAC systems, can make this strategy more practical.

CONCLUSION

The economics of growing depends on many factors, not least of which is the environment you choose to grow in. There are currently four ways to grow viably in North America:

1. No enclosure (outdoor grow)
2. Greenhouse without artificial lighting
3. Mixed-light greenhouse
4. Warehouse without sunlight

These facilities all have benefits and downsides, so picking the right one for you should be a business decision based on what offers the best return on investment. Growing outside costs less but includes many risks inherent to lack of total control. The cost of growing tends to scale upwards in concert with the level of control you give yourself, right up to a fully enclosed warehouse structure. The warehouse offers maximum control, which contributes to higher yield volumes, quality, and consistency, but also includes higher capital and operating costs. Make sure you understand all the pros and cons and model the costs before choosing a facility type. Many growers have made assumptions before knowing all the costs and ended up with facilities that either do not produce the results they are hoping for, or are significantly more expensive to renovate and operate than initially budgeted.

Another consideration is whether to build a new structure or to retrofit an old building. Again, there are numerous pros and cons. Retrofitting is usually less expensive and can enable a quicker start-up, but brings many challenges caused by shoehorning a cannabis operation into a facility not designed to accommodate such an activity. Purpose-built facilities are generally able to include more of the design ideas that can lead to better outcomes for both crop quality and the bottom line.

Incorporating scalability and redundancy into your facility is a key part of business success, by both reducing risk and by making it easier to scale-up in the future over both the short and long term.

NAVIGATING THE TRADITIONAL EQUIPMENT PROCUREMENT PROCESS

CHAPTER 05

Designing and installing the right equipment into a project is far more complex than most growers would expect. The process itself sets the stage for conflicting interests between lowest initial cost and smartest long-term value, a critical balance for owners!

This topic is especially important when it comes to selecting the HVAC equipment that will control your grow room environment. HVAC is one of the most significant costs of running a grow room. For most growers, utilities, including the energy to run their HVAC, is their second biggest operating expense after payroll.

A grow room HVAC system is a mission-critical investment in the health of your business that, in many cases, has not been given the focus it deserves. The right type of equipment can make a serious difference in the quality, quantity, and consistency of your harvest. It can also mitigate the risks of mold and other related diseases.

Of equal importance is operating efficiency, equipment life expectancy, reliability and maintenance costs. All of these factors will have a significant impact on the success and profitability of your business.

The operational math of growing cannabis is strongly in favor of making smart HVAC investments and choosing high-quality equipment that conserves energy, performs reliably and lasts a long time.

The additional cost of superior equipment can often be recovered in the first year. Over a 10 or 15-year period, the return on a quality grow room HVAC system can be hundreds of thousands of dollars in both operational savings and increased revenue due to higher quality and more consistent crop.

Many growers have found the traditional equipment procurement process, with its many levels and interested parties such as engineers, vendors, and contractors, to be opaque and confusing to navigate. The result is that many growers are not getting involved in a buying decision that has such a large potential impact upon their business. They may end up with the lowest upfront cost, rather than the equipment that delivers the best value. As we will explore throughout this chapter, there can be a big difference between the two.

To be clear, we have a definite bias in the content that follows. Fortunately, that bias is toward delivering exactly the math we mentioned earlier: the optimal balance of capital cost, installation costs, maintenance and operating costs to deliver outstanding ROI. We also have a bias toward scalability, redundancy, reliability, and long-lasting equipment that will deliver the lowest total cost of ownership.

Because there are so many participants in the process with different levels of HVAC design knowledge and potentially competing interests, the design, specification, and equipment selection process can be very convoluted. There are many decision points, which may not always serve the owner's best interests.

There are no hard and fast rules for HVAC, but for new construction and often for repurposing existing buildings for cannabis production, the process is as follows:

1. The owner selects an architect to design or retrofit a building.
2. The architect hires an engineering firm to manage all facets of engineering.
3. The engineering firm may hire an HVAC specialist to design HVAC requirements.
4. The engineering firm/HVAC specialist invites rep firm vendors to recommend HVAC solutions and propose equipment options.
5. Rep firms propose various solutions, price points, and may require manufacturer support (few rep firms are experts in all equipment lines they represent).

6. The engineer accepts a proposed solution and uses that solution to create their "basis of design" specification for the bidding process.
7. The general contractor is hired by the owner, architect, or engineering firm to build the project, typically through a price-sensitive bidding process.
8. The winning general contractor solicits bids from sub-contractors specializing in various aspects of the job (another price-sensitive process).
9. The winning sub-contractor typically gets the job based on best price to supply and install the HVAC equipment that "meets the specifications" set out by the engineer. (Of note, there can be several vendors and several levels of quality that will technically meet specifications; the sub-contractor may be motivated to choose the lowest cost in order to maximize their profits).
10. The winning sub-contractor typically must support the installed equipment for only one year after start-up. This short-term window of product support means the contractor may be less concerned with long-term product viability.

Although there are often variances, the 10 steps outlined above are the most common. The key take-away is that there are two main hurdles that growers face:

- Those involved in the process are often not grow room experts and don't always know the "right" equipment choice.
- The contractor who buys the equipment is often hired at a fixed price and may be motivated to procure the lowest-cost equipment that technically meets the engineer's specifications, to maximize their profit. The result often does not offer the best value.

Unless the architect, owner, engineer, or general contractor directs the HVAC sub-contractor to purchase a specific brand of equipment, or use a particular technology, the final equipment selection takes place at the end of the process and may be subject to factors that result in less than ideal equipment selection.

Why? Because the contractor has already bid and won the job based on their predetermined price; any additional savings they can extract will add to their profits from the project, thus they are typically looking to meet the specifications of the job with the lowest-cost equipment they can find.

DEFINING EQUIPMENT "VALUE"

The word "value" can mean many different things to many different people. The Gage dictionary defines value as a noun, meaning "worth; excellence; usefulness; importance."

This is a good place to start, but we need something more specific to define equipment value for the cannabis grower.

For us, value means a product that maximizes return on investment by providing the best performance and the lowest overall cost of ownership.

This tangible value is easy to evaluate as follows:

1. Equipment purchase price: initial capital costs of equipment.
2. Installation costs: ease of installation and related costs.
3. Operating costs: energy consumption.
4. Maintenance costs: regular maintenance costs and system risk mitigation.

5. Repair costs: cost to repair or replace key components, including warranties or special extended service agreements.
6. Lifetime of service: life expectancy of equipment.

Other considerations include:

7. Scalability: room by room expansion, facility growth, incremental stages.
8. Reliability: likelihood of failure, ease of repair.
9. Redundancy: built-in failover or multiple independent refrigeration circuits to prevent total failure.

These are all costs that could be higher or lower depending on the type and brand of equipment and the technology or type of HVAC solution.

Another important tangible value of equipment is in the impact it has on your grow. If selecting a certain kind of equipment can improve your yield and your quality each by just 2%, what kind of value does that lend to your business: 5%? 10%?

When deciding which equipment to buy, it's critical to look at the total cost of ownership to understand the fullest picture of the cost vs. benefit.

There is considerable misunderstanding about the difference between the lowest upfront (first) cost and the total cost of ownership (i.e., best product value). That drives many to select whatever offers the lowest upfront cost.

At the end of the day, choosing equipment is an investment in the health of the facility and business. There are a variety of HVAC options on the market today. While they all seek to do the same process, they do not all perform the same way, and performance of the equipment is what really matters here. A facility can certainly reduce initial capital costs by buying a cheaper solution. But they will end up with underperforming equipment that offers a shorter lifespan with higher energy/operating and maintenance costs.

Cannabis projects are very expensive and the pressure to reduce costs as much as possible is understandable. But does it make sense to skimp on such a critical issue as HVAC, which will affect your business over the long term? Saving $20,000 on HVAC for a multi-million-dollar grow facility can easily sabotage the success of the business and reduce your bottom line.

Limited budgets are an unavoidable reality, but those precious dollars need to be allocated appropriately.

LOW COST IS USUALLY VERY EXPENSIVE

Equipment specifications rarely include energy consumption criteria, operating, maintenance or service costs, nor do they factor reliability or equipment life, all of which have a huge impact on the most important long-term value considerations. In fact, many engineers will typically create a very generic specification that does not spell out competitive features. The result is that almost any equipment could be said to "meet" the specifications. And, unless a non-traditional extended warranty is called for, grow facility managers are saddled with the long-term outcome of their equipment choices. This cost should be a big concern to owners.

Owners need to be aware of the exact equipment specified by the engineer and from which vendor/brand. If the equipment is premium quality, will the contractor be allowed to supply alternatives or substitutions? Specifications must be extremely precise, with key competitive features clearly defined in the documentation.

Obtaining a premium quality solution to their HVAC needs is one of the biggest challenges facing owners. In our estimation, lowest "first cost" or lowest cost on "contractor bid day" is typically not the smartest money or the best way to ensure the best long-term value and performance.

We highly recommend that owners have a clear understanding of the entire HVAC decision process from design to installation. Ask many questions, understand the options, and explore the specific recommendations. Get all the facts.

Another critical, but often under-addressed aspect of effective HVAC design, is the air distribution ductwork design. The sad fact is that no matter how effective the performance of the HVAC equipment, if the air distribution is flawed, the plants will not experience the right conditions. The ducting and diffusers must be sized and designed appropriately for the volume of air the HVAC equipment will provide. Both must be designed in concert to achieve optimal results; some manufacturers provide much higher airflow than others, which has a serious impact on system design.

A well-informed owner, architect, or engineer can predetermine the brand of HVAC equipment or type of HVAC design they prefer. However, it makes no sense that the final decision should come down to the lowest cost without consideration of the bigger picture equipment value factors. As the owner or master grower, you will be well-advised to understand and participate in the decision process for the entirety of the HVAC design and specification.

Like any other product, HVAC systems are available from different brands at varying price points and quality. They may be built with different materials and components or use different technologies. Some have proprietary systems that offer facilities a competitive edge, like internet monitoring technology or unique energy-saving features, built-in redundancy, etc.

In many ways, buying an HVAC system is like buying a new car. Nobody would say that all cars are the same. Yes, they all intend to get you from point A to point B, but some do it better than others. Some offer you a smoother or a safer ride.

They may have a better reputation for quality and longevity or offer more fuel efficiency. These are the kind of factors that most people consider when buying a car. The same criteria apply to HVAC purchases.

THE ROI FROM SMART HVAC DECISIONS

Certain kinds of equipment can save a facility more money in operating expenses. This breaks down in two main ways.

Energy efficiency: HVAC has high energy needs, and some manufacturers have smart technologies to significantly reduce these energy requirements to offer facilities a lower cost of ownership.

For example, the right dehumidifier can recycle latent heat from the grow room air to pre-heat the dehumidification coil's cold discharge air before it goes back into the space. Given that dehumidification requires very cold temperatures in order to dry the air, sending the chilled air directly into the space without heating it back up could shock the plants and stunt growth. By recycling existing energy in the grow space, you can avoid or reduce use of costly auxiliary heaters.

The equipment could also use economizer cooling technology to save from 15% to 30% on annual energy costs, depending on location. New technology today allows this cooling without introducing any outdoor air into the space, thus eliminating the possibility of contaminating plants. Considering that energy costs are one of the largest financial expenses for growers, this 15% to 30% savings is significant.

As covered in Chapter 2, there has been a tendency to misapply equipment in the grow space. Using the wrong type of equipment, such as regular commercial air conditioners or central chillers, looks good because it is cheap to buy and quick to set up. But it may be the wrong solution for grow rooms as these products are not typically designed for the exacting requirements of growing cannabis and might not deliver expected performance. For example, commercial air conditioners typically are unable to address humidity loads, as their coils are only designed to address temperature.

In order to condense water out of the air, you must cool (subtract heat from) the air by a certain amount. Much of that is sensible heat that a thermometer reads. But after a certain amount of sensible heat is removed, you must then remove latent heat — the energy contained within moisture — to condense moisture out of the air. Dehumidifiers are designed to do that by putting a higher priority on latent cooling, achieving this with unique construction elements not usually found in air conditioning coils. As a result, they are usually better suited to cool to the degree required to affect the phase change from vapor to liquid.

Failing to control humidity could result in stunted growth for the plants. Therefore, although the initial cost may be low, the ongoing cost of ownership turns out to be quite high for misapplied equipment.

The type of HVAC equipment is also important. Selecting a good quality, unitary dehumidification and air conditioning system can take advantage of those money-saving energy recycling technologies. A unitary dehumidifier can provide air conditioning and humidity control, while also pre-heating return air, all in one unit. Non-unitary approaches have separate pieces to handle these different functions, resulting in systems that fight each other and create inefficiencies. Another benefit of choosing small unitary systems is that they are typically cheaper to install, run, and maintain than one large system. They can also be designed to run as separate systems in multiples to provide improved redundancy.

Not only can the right equipment save money by being more efficient and lasting longer, it can even bring in more income.

Effective HVAC has a major impact on a grower's crop quality, volume, and consistency, which in turn produces more revenue. Equipment that has a handle on dehumidification will ensure a quality crop; equipment that does not achieve dehumidification well can lead to inconsistent crops at best and diseased or dead crop at worst.

For example, ineffective equipment can allow humidity levels to get too high, which could leave crop open to mold. Too much humidity also reduces the rate at which crop grows, because plants cannot efficiently transpire when air is too moist. Likewise, if the HVAC reduces humidity too much, crop growth will slow as it enters drought-resistant mode. If you have a system that is removing too much humidity, a supplemental humidifier will need to be added to the space, which obviously will bring with it added costs to buy and operate. Clearly, humidity control is a fine art that requires precision equipment to get right.

What are the benefits of consistent crop? For growers, this plays into brand identity. The world's most successful businesses, certainly in the consumable products sector, have built their success at least partially on consistency. The names McDonald's, Starbucks and Coca-Cola come to mind. These are brands known for their consistency, a trait that no doubt contributes to their success in the marketplace. As the field of growers becomes more crowded, consistency will be a brand differentiator. In particular, those pursuing exclusive supply agreements will want to pay attention to both speed of growth and consistency of product as they seek lucrative contracts. A grow space with the right HVAC equipment enables that product.

SO, HOW TO GET THE RIGHT EQUIPMENT?

Designing commercial-scale cannabis grow rooms is still a new frontier and technologies are changing constantly. There's also a considerable level of secrecy and competitive confidentiality relating to what works, causing a serious information vacuum in this area.

Clearly, there's a lot of pioneering work being done that is not setting industry standards. This is very different than the traditional construction industry, where the American Society of Heating and Refrigeration Engineers (ASHRAE) sets standards. General construction is not a competitive business with trade secrets guarded in the same way that growing cannabis is. ASHRAE so far has no engineering standards or best practices published about how to design for grow rooms.

Even the technically qualified engineering firms have to guess at a considerable amount of the science and mechanics behind creating optimal grow environments. Designing a grow room is extremely complex and involves considerably more variables than designing traditional HVAC systems for commercial buildings.

Getting grow room equipment specification right requires careful modeling of grow cycles, transpiration rates, temperature and humidity specifications, lighting loads, and irrigation loads, just to name a few. It also requires careful modeling of external factors, including annual temperature and humidity ranges, type of building structure, and so on.

All of these factors must be carefully modeled to ensure that HVAC engineering specifications can be met.

Unfortunately, as discussed in Chapter 2, there is a severe knowledge deficit among engineers regarding HVAC. The lack of standards to provide guidance on these issues has created an inconsistency of knowledge and the result is that many engineers are ill-equipped to handle the grow space's unique demands.

Although selecting the equipment with a lower initial cost is tempting, this is not usually the best value. It's better to look at what will save you money later in ongoing operating and maintenance costs. Often, selected equipment gets pared down and its energy-saving features eliminated to reduce costs. This "value engineering" should be approached cautiously and avoided if it would increase the operating cost of the equipment.

WHO DO YOU TRUST?

Given the inconsistency of knowledge in the industry today, there are not many sources of expertise on grow rooms that cannabis companies can access. Growers are certainly knowledgeable about plant science, but most are not experts on building design, HVAC applications, and systems control.

There is no shortage of people trying to provide support to growers on these issues. Engineers have become involved with cannabis as a direct result of legalization, as a grower would not be able to get a municipal building permit without the involvement of a professional engineer. Many vendors are pushing product "solutions" that are simply repurposed from other applications and may not work in the grow environment.

Erasmus of Rotterdam's ancient proverb, "In the land of the blind, the one-eyed man is king," (originally in Latin) applies to the grow industry. It's difficult for growers to discern who are the true experts because so many people are jumping onto the cannabis bandwagon and offering well-intentioned but often flawed solutions.

Who do you trust? Who are the real experts?

You also must question who is looking out for growers in this wild marketplace. Everybody is looking to get their own slice of the pie and maximizing profit is the name of the game.

There is a phenomenon observed throughout the grow industry called the "marijuana mark-up," a somewhat sensitive topic among circles adjacent to the industry. It refers to the perception among growers that some in the equipment supply and installation industry are looking to take advantage of cash-rich growers. Many growers are trying to scale-up as quickly as possible, and some vendors may be motivated to take advantage of this rush, adding substantial mark-ups to their equipment.

Therefore, the grower really needs to get involved in the procurement process and not shy away from spelling out exactly what they want. If they leave it to the "experts," the results may be disappointing.

In short, nobody is looking out for you. It's entirely up to you, the grower, to make sure you find what you need.

We have written this book specifically to ensure that growers like you are able to learn from mistakes in the industry and get an inside look at the equipment selection and procurement process to avoid these consequences. We've been involved in the dehumidification business for over 40 years and have been supplying HVAC equipment for a very long time. We understand the challenges currently facing the grow industry because we're deeply involved in it. We created this book to share our knowledge because we know we can help, and we know that knowledgeable customers are happy customers.

EXPLORING THE SOLUTIONS

With so many conflicting interests in the procurement process, and few people who are knowledgeable enough about grow rooms to make the right decision, the odds of owners getting the right equipment seems slim. But you own the process and can get what you want if you know how to take control of it.

When the design team is assembled, hold an initial meeting to go over your expectations for how the facility will function. Everybody needs to be on the same page. Capturing details in writing is a crucial step to ensuring everyone is working towards the same, clearly stated goals.

Ask many of questions and make sure you're getting clear, accurate answers. Understand the reasons for certain recommendations. Get a lay of the land and all the options that are available to you. Make sure you know all the facts.

We'll explain more about getting the design right in Chapters 6, 7, and 8. For now, you need to know that it's a collaborative effort, but the owner is in control.

You may leave equipment specification and selection to the engineer and contractor, respectively. But, as noted, this comes with some risks. As an owner, there are varying levels of a hands-on approach you can take to minimize the risk of poor or inappropriate HVAC design and less than ideal equipment or technologies.

One approach is to direct your engineer to be tight with their specs. Often, engineer specs are vague and spell out just the minimum of requirements, like what room temperature and relative humidity the equipment should be able to maintain. In other words, these are "unspecific specifications."

Instead, have them nail down key competitive features of the equipment. Differentiators that would benefit you need to be outlined in black and white with explanations, including:

1. Solution Design: What kind of a system will be used? It could be an all-in-one unitary system, or sensible cooling devices like rooftop air conditioners, or a central plant chilled water system that would need to be paired with standalone dehumidifiers.
2. Airflow: CFM to the room to ensure sufficient air changes (ideally X per minute or Y per ton of capacity).
3. Duct and diffuser design: to ensure 100% optimal airflow and distribution to the room and canopy to match the CFM.
4. Detailed load calculations: based on accurate lighting loads, plant densities, room conditions, ambient conditions, watering and transpiration loads, etc.
5. Energy consumption: estimates based on specific design elements.

An engineer must review a proposed solution in detail to ensure it meets the spec.

Make sure specifications are detailed and precise, providing more than just room temperature and relative humidity.

Another option that owners have is a flat spec, where a well-informed owner tells the engineer exactly what kind of equipment they want. If the owner feels strongly about a particular equipment brand, they can have the engineer ensure that only equipment from that brand is selected for the project. Although this seems intimidating for the nontechnical, it's quite easy. Manufacturer websites spell out their equipment features and benefits in plain English. With the information throughout this book, you'll be equipped with the insights you need to make this decision with confidence.

CONCLUSION

Buying HVAC equipment is a complex endeavor. Not many people can call themselves grow room experts because the industry is still very new, and no standards exist yet to provide engineers with guidance on how to approach design for building systems.

It makes no sense that equipment decisions should be made based on lowest cost, rather than in the context of big-picture equipment value factors. Not all equipment is made equal and owners should be aware of the differences between superior and inferior equipment. Total cost of ownership, including installation cost, energy cost, warranty, serviceability, and maintenance requirements, should be the main consideration when buying. Do not look solely at the first cost. Additionally, the owner should be involved in making the purchase decision to ensure that the decision is 100% motivated by what would benefit the business in the long term, rather than others involved in the process.

Owners need to have a clear understanding of the procurement process in place, from design to installation. Everyone on the design team needs to be on the same page and the owner should communicate their expectations in writing.

It's quite easy for the owner to take control of the process, if they understand how it works. Directing the engineer to use particular technologies, or to buy a specific brand of equipment, is well within the realm of a well-informed owner.

At the end of the day, the grower should take charge of the equipment procurement process to make sure the right solution is installed.

PROPER SIZING OF HVAC

CHAPTER 06

Ensuring that HVAC equipment is properly sized for its grow room application is critical for growers, as it will help define the success and profitability of your operation.

Avoid improperly sized equipment. Units that are too big cost more to buy and use far more energy than necessary and could possibly result in an over-cooled or over-dried space. Similarly, equipment that is too small will be unable to keep up with demand and result in space conditions such as overheating or excess humidity, and these issues could potentially reduce crop quality or put plants in danger.

Given the many variables at play in grow rooms, significantly more than in standard environments, and considering most engineers are unfamiliar with this specific application, sizing calculations for grow room HVAC has been a very challenging task. This is largely due to misinformation and a lack of knowledge among those involved in the facility design industry.

Even the most technically-qualified engineering firms have had to guess at a considerable amount of the science and mechanics behind creating optimal grow environments due to a lack of HVAC design standards for engineers, and because the cannabis industry is so secretive about what works and what does not. In this industry, engineering jobs are extremely complex and involve dozens more variables than designing traditional HVAC systems for commercial buildings.

Getting grow room specifications right requires careful modeling of grow cycles, transpiration rates, temperature and humidity specifications, lighting loads, and irrigation loads, just to name a few. It also requires careful modeling of external factors, including annual temperature and humidity ranges, type of building structure, solar impacts of mixed-light sources, etc. Some of these factors may vary by type of plant and strain, which only further complicates the matter.

THE UNITARY ADVANTAGE

Unitary solutions can provide all the systems you need in one. Air conditioning with dehumidification priority offers superior functionality and advantages for growers compared to simple air conditioners that can't typically meet the moisture-removal demands of the growing environment. Separate cooling and dehumidification systems, regardless of size, may be difficult to tie together and counteract one another and can be very inefficient, while also delivering inferior results and increased costs for the grower.

One advantage of unitary equipment is that you can use a different unit for each grow room, which may be used for different strains or stages and thus likely have varying needs. This option provides great scalability and flexibility for the grower, while making it easier to properly size equipment to the needs of each individual room.

> A great advantage of the unitary system design is that multiple units can serve the same room, preventing any single point of failure. The risk reduction and peace of mind for growers is priceless.

In order to properly model conditions, you need to have a clear idea of what each room needs: Is it a mother room? Or flowering? What kind of watering system will be in use? How does transpiration rate change throughout the day and throughout each grow stage?

Choosing energy-efficient equipment is extremely important, as the grow industry already has a very large energy footprint.

Reducing energy usage as much as possible by investing in smart technologies will benefit you greatly over time. Because unitary systems roll everything into one, they can recycle heat created by their processes; for example, they can divert energy from hot compressor gas into pre-heating the cold air that comes off the dehumidifier coil before it goes back into the space.

Although selecting the equipment with a lower capital cost is tempting, this is not usually the best value. You must also consider installation costs when looking at the overall system. In addition, consider the money saved later in ongoing operating and maintenance costs. Often, chosen equipment gets pared down and its energy-saving features eliminated to reduce upfront costs. This "value engineering" should be approached cautiously and avoided if it increases the operating cost of the equipment.

CAREFUL COST-BENEFIT MODELING

Central chilled water plants are a tried-and-true solution for projects requiring large refrigeration capacity. They are found in college campuses, hospitals, office buildings, and other large facilities. But while central chillers are a good default for most large-scale applications, they may fall short for the cannabis industry. Central chillers need very careful consideration before being used for this application, because they probably are not the best solution for a grow facility.

If the grower knows the exact size of facility they need, and the required conditions match the capability of a chilled water system, then it could be a viable HVAC option. However, getting it right can be expensive.

Chillers are usually simple systems in large facilities that do not demand much dehumidification. For example, data centers are great candidates for chillers because they only need standard air conditioning with no need for reheating or auxiliary heat, so a simple two-pipe system can be used.

The challenge with a grow space is the humidity. To properly control the space conditions and dehumidify effectively, you need to cool the air down to much colder temperatures in order to more effectively condense the humidity out of the air. That means a chilled water temperature needs to be much colder than is traditional, which turns out to be very inefficient when using the typical chilled water air handlers and chillers mentioned above. Furthermore, in lights-out mode, you need to be able to not just dry the air (cool it off enough to condense moisture out) but you then must reheat it, so as to not overcool the grow room. Energy recovery can be used to provide the reheat function for free. If an HVAC system doesn't do that, then operating costs will be higher.

As a result of the need to reheat air, a chiller must include a boiler, along with another set of pipes and a more complicated and expensive installation. The inexpensive two-pipe system now becomes a much more expensive and complicated four-pipe system. You also need to run your chiller well below its most efficient operating point, then add heat from an auxiliary source (such as a boiler), and then incorporate sophisticated systems to control all of it. There may also be a desire to add redundancy to your chiller, your pumps, and your boiler so that you have no single point of failure for your entire complex. Otherwise, the central plant is a major liability.

Before selecting a central chilled water plant design, the design team should use cost-benefit modeling to weigh the pros and cons of that choice over a unitary design.

SOME FACTORS TO CONSIDER

As noted, there are numerous influencers of proper HVAC equipment sizing. Because most engineers do not have the knowledge to model them and select the right size, they will rely on equipment manufacturers to provide accurate sizing. Manufacturers know their equipment and would be best placed to advise on its application.

Each manufacturer may have their own form to fill out with key variables. Here are some examples:

- Room dimensions
- Purpose (mother, clone, etc.)
- Building material
- Temperature and RH at beginning and end of grow
- Lighting type and wattage per square foot of active grow
- Active grow area (as a percentage of room volume)
- Number of plants or plant density
- Watering rate per plant per day
- Type of watering system

For your own benefit, you should know all of these factors before beginning your HVAC equipment buying process. You should be able to provide this information, openly and honestly, to your manufacturer so that they can provide the best solution for your needs.

If you have confidentiality concerns, it is acceptable to ask for the manufacturer to sign a nondisclosure agreement; companies sign these all the time. But they do need the information one way or another.

Lighting intensity expressed in wattage per square foot is one key metric that growers often have not decided when they look into buying their HVAC system. Because the lighting wattage is the biggest source of energy into the space, it's actually going to have a large impact on the size of the HVAC system; therefore, this is a detail that needs to be worked out before you approach an HVAC manufacturer. More details on lighting are found in Chapter 7.

Room dimensions are important for the manufacturer but are not the only variable they need to know.

Unusual for this application is the fact that the airflow volume is dictated by equipment capacity and not room volume. Clearly, the HVAC manufacturer cannot determine the appropriate equipment capacity based only on floor space; how would they be able to account for heat load from the lights or humidity produced by plant transpiration? That's why it's so important for you to be open with your vendor and have a frank discussion about how you are going to be running the building.

Prudent decisions about every element of the grow room are essential to maximizing profit and product quality. One example is the lighting system. Although LED lights are not yet an industry norm, they are an effective way to lower your HVAC costs because they create less heat. You would be able to save 30% of electricity just running the lights, plus achieve a 30% reduction in sensible heat load on the HVAC, which by extension allows for smaller equipment that costs less to purchase and operate. The compounding savings may make it worthwhile to go for LED, despite the higher upfront cost.

When retrofitting a facility that was designed for high-intensity discharge lighting, there may be an opportunity to increase yields by installing LED that uses the same power density for much greater lighting intensity. Although this research is relatively new, LED may be an effective way for growers to use existing facilities to their full potential.

CONCLUSION

Work closely with your HVAC design engineers to discuss and incorporate all factors that will affect temperature and humidity loads into your ideal specifications. Be certain that they work with the equipment manufacturer to properly model the dozens of load factors and variations that your plants and your grow cycles will require.

Before you connect with your manufacturer, it's important to have a clear idea on how you are going to run the facility and have solid knowledge about key factors that influence HVAC sizing. When you do, be sure to provide them with all of the information and specifications they need in order to provide you with the best solution.

Seeking energy-efficient products is a good idea for positive long-term business outcomes. Especially since growing cannabis consumes so much energy, investing in some smart technologies can save you considerable costs over time.

GETTING THE BEST GROW CONDITIONS

CHAPTER 07

A great grow room environment will play a big role in providing your operation with high yields and quality crop. Because cannabis requires a lot of love and care to grow, providing a properly controlled space depends on numerous factors.

This chapter provides some general tips and guidelines for growers to keep in mind when creating their growing environment. Key to the entire design process, of course, is knowing exactly what you want and why; you are simply not going to get anywhere productive without a very clear picture of your goals.

SO, WHAT *DO* YOU WANT?

The grower needs to consider what kind of product they are producing in a given room. Is the finished product to be dried bud? Or are you planning to extract? These are two examples of how the end product may dictate different conditions in the grow room.

For example, with extract, the temperature and RH levels typically do not change significantly from the beginning of the grow to the end.

For the purposes of extract, many growers are typically less concerned about color or smell (i.e. terpene content) because these factors will not make a difference for the end user. But if you're producing bud, these things do matter; most people are picky about their cannabis and may not buy it if the color is unusual or the smell is unpleasant. Temperature and RH levels can vary widely throughout the grow stages, so the HVAC needs to be able to deliver those conditions.

Most growers are chasing one big goal: yield. More yield can translate into bigger profits due to economies of scale and the fact you have more product to sell. If that is indeed what you seek, it's important to understand what can lead to that outcome.

When a grower tells us they are looking for more yield, what we hear is that they need precise room conditions that allow plants to grow as efficiently as possible.

If you are to have any hope of achieving this result, there are some things you need to have figured out before shopping for an HVAC system. It's not enough to know your square footage. As an HVAC manufacturer, we have a set of factors we need to know in order to supply the right equipment. These factors are listed in the previous chapter. Any manufacturer you are dealing with should provide their own list of necessary information to help you choose the best solution for your needs.

LIGHTING

The biggest driver of your HVAC system will be the lighting, because it creates significant sensible heat that has a wide-ranging effect on the space loads. This heat needs to be removed with air conditioning, a highly energy-intensive process.

We refer to both "sensible" and "latent" heat throughout this book. Understanding the difference is important for selecting HVAC. Sensible heat is the kind of heat that can be measured by a thermometer. Latent heat is energy required to cause a phase change, but not a change in temperature. In the grow room context, latent heat refers to moisture in the air.

What kind of lighting will you use? A great variety of lighting types is available to growers. Some of them are geared towards a specific stage of the growing cycle, whereas others have a more universal application. There is considerable debate in the grow industry about certain types of lighting and their uses, particularly with LED. Although some growers are skeptical about the benefits of LED, we believe that the industry should be open to considering alternatives beyond the traditional lighting arrangements that have been used, with little change, since the 1980s.

WHAT KIND OF LIGHT?

As all growers know very well, light is one of the critical elements required for a plant to grow, as it enables photosynthesis, the plant's way of creating energy. Detailed understanding of the intricacies at play in plant photobiology continues to evolve and remains subject to much research. Applying the established science to commercial cannabis production continues to be a challenge, though there have been improvements in the past few years. Limited study on cannabis, due to legal issues, has long been a barrier.

There are three key influencers of light in photosynthesis:

- Wavelength
- Intensity
- Duration of exposure (i.e., photoperiod). The amount of time a plant is exposed to light vs. darkness plays a role in its development because it signals the time for the plant to progress to further stages of growth.

Light is also an influencer of photomorphogenesis, a separate phenomenon to photosynthesis. While photosynthesis refers to the process where light enables a plant to create energy, photomorphogenesis refers to how light affects plant development. They're hard to distinguish from each other, but the outcome of a plant under any type of light is dependent on the combined effects of the two.[29]

Plants are technically responsive to all visible wavelengths of light, as is the human eye. The visible range extends approximately from 380–740 nanometers. Plants are typically responsive to a similar range of light, demonstrated in the McCree Curve that extends from 360–760 nm, with the most important part ranging from 400–700 nm. However, there is some difference in the type of light each uses. Human eyes are especially sensitive to green light, whereas plants have been observed to be more responsive to blue and red light.[29] Light originating from the sun is a pure white, meaning it contains all spectrums of visible light as well as wavelengths outside the visible range, like ultraviolet and infrared. Because white light contains the full visible range of colors, you can pass it through a prism to split them up and create a rainbow. Light from artificial sources can be white, but it will only be similar to the sun; no artificial lighting has yet been developed for commercial grow use that exactly matches the attributes of sunlight.

The lack of detailed research specifically on cannabis photobiology has created an evidence gap in this field of study. Varied research by McCree and Inada demonstrated that red and far-red light (wavelengths longer than 600 nm) are the most efficient for photosynthesis for plants in general because their pigments absorb red light more readily.[30]

This research corresponds with standard use of HPs lighting for the flowering stage of cannabis.

Experience among cannabis growers has shown that plants that are exposed to blue light in vegetation stage, when they are forming roots and stock, are typically thicker and stronger than those that are not exposed to this type of light.

This effect is consistent with other types of plant. Blue light also tempers the plant's tendency to grow long; plants grown with blue light are usually more compact than those mainly exposed to red light.

Yorio et al. (2001) tried growing radish, lettuce, and spinach hydroponically under red-light LEDs and compared to plants grown under cool-white fluorescent lamps and red LEDs plus 10% blue LED light.[31] At harvest, the plants grown with only red light had significantly less yield in dry weight than those grown under either fluorescent or red plus 10% blue LED. The crop grown under fluorescent also did significantly better in yield than those grown under red plus 10% blue LED.

This result added to an existing body of research that demonstrates blue light is important to plant development. However, it's still an open question how much is needed. Also, responsiveness to blue light appears to vary by plant species.

Blue light may also affect cannabinoid content. Magagnini et al. (2018) grew cannabis sativa plants under three types of lighting: high-pressure sodium vapor (HPS), as well as AP673L and NS1 type LED lights.[32] HPS light is a yellow-red hue with minimal blue wavelengths, while the LED lights put out some of both red and blue. AP673L leans more to red while NS1 has more blue intensity.

The researchers rooted the plant clones for two weeks under T8 fluorescent lights and then, after transplanting, placed them under 18 hours daily of HPS light for 8 days as they acclimatized. In the vegetation stage, the plants were then subjected to their respective experimental light type, for 18 hours during vegetation for 13 days and then 12 hours light and 12 hours dark for 46 days of flowering.

In terms of dry flower weight yield, the Magagnini study suggested red-dominant HPS light may produce more because there is minimal blue light to limit morphology of the plants. On the other hand, crop grown under the two LED light types appeared to gain improved cannabinoid content over those grown under HPS. There was no significant difference noted between the types of LED and corresponding cannabinoid content.

Green light is typically not considered by growers as it is known to be the least efficient color for photosynthesis. However, green light is known to penetrate the deepest into the leaf.[33] Some studies have shown green light can counter blue light's limiting of stem elongation by deactivating cryptochromes. Kaiser et al. (2019) published a study in Scientia Horticulturae that experimented with adding green light to a crop of tomatoes.[34] The researchers wrote: "Partially replacing a red:blue spectrum by green increased biomass by up to 6.5% … Green tended to increase leaf biomass, specific leaf area, stem biomass and length." HPS does not produce much green light, but a grower interested in leveraging the effects of green light would be able to get it by using broad spectrum LED.

Further adding to the evidence in support of providing cannabis with broad-spectrum white light is a paper published in 2019, The Impact of Light Intensity and Spectrum-Tuning on Cannabis Yields (SSRN), by James Eaves of the University of Laval Department of Management, et al.[35]

The Eaves paper stated: "We find no evidence that the various tuned spectrums offered by specialty horticulture LED lights increase yields compared to the much less expensive, general purpose, broad-spectrum LED lights. It took less time for the LED treatments to reach peak ripeness, and the resulting morphology of plants grown under high-intensity LEDs is more desirable from a profitability perspective."

Researchers support increasing the intensity of LED lighting significantly to improve yields: "The positive, apparently linear relationship between intensity and yields continues to at least 1,500 μmols/m2/s, which is over twice the level provided by an HPs fixture in a grow configuration, which is currently the industry standard."

Typically, LED lights are run at lower intensities than HPS because the main benefit of LED is as an energy-saver. The Eaves paper, however, suggested that it may be worth spending more on electricity to run high intensity LED lights given the improved yield. The grower could do that, or they could just use HPS-equivalent LED intensities to strike a balance between yield and lower operating costs. At normal intensity, LED could save 30%+ on electricity to run the lights as well as reduced load on the HVAC system.

The complicated balancing act of lighting rests entirely with the grower but must be clearly factored into HVAC calculations.

AIRSIDE SOLUTIONS

With a lighting system in mind, you then need to turn your attention to the airside requirements, which includes air distribution, airflow, and type of ductwork, to name a few.

Engineers will have some familiarity with airside factors. Like any HVAC application, the goal is to move air through the space.

The only difference from a traditional environment is, instead of delivering fresh oxygen-rich air to humans, you are delivering air saturated with CO_2 to plants. Growers are typically providing 2–3 times more CO_2 in the air than ambient, to ensure that it is not a limiting factor in growth.

The airflow should be at a high velocity. In fact, the airflow should have those leaves dancing: we cannot allow any air to stagnate around the leaves and create ultra-microclimates.

A typical recommendation is to shoot air to the plants at between .5 and 1 m/s. There are two ways to accomplish this with the duct design. In both cases, the air needs to be warm to keep the plants from cooling through the transpiration process and forming condensation, which could promote mold.

One strategy is to position air diffusers on one side of the room and the return on the opposite end. This provides a linear airflow in one direction and works best in small rooms because the air velocity would be reduced over a greater distance. Additionally, you may experience some variation in the temperature from the diffuser to the return. One way to account for this is to break up the room by sectors and provide multiple diffusers and returns.

Another air distribution method is to place the air system in the growing tiers themselves. This is effective for larger rooms as well as multi-tier rooms where there are several layers of plants. However, rearranging the tiers after the fact is nearly impossible without expensive modifications and reengineering.

Whatever system you choose, keep in mind that the air distribution pattern must be an engineered system that is specifically designed to eliminate the possibility of any stagnant air around the plants. One thing to avoid is air tunnels running through open aisles in the grow space. The plants will act as a wall to prevent the air from reaching deeply into the plant area. It's much better to put your diffusers where they will easily reach the leaves.

Advancements in computational fluid dynamics means there are now services available to create a computational model of airflow in grow rooms. Although it may seem like a significant upfront expense, the expertise generated by going through this exercise can provide outstanding return on investment. Some equipment vendors may bundle this service with their products.

The air churn needs to come entirely from the distribution.

The grow room is quite unusual in that it requires 40–50 air changes per hour, whereas most other spaces need fewer than 10.

Do not rely on band-aid solutions here, like the all-too common application of supplemental fans to improve circulation. These are cheap but risky: they're difficult to clean and can lead to contamination. As well, they add heat to the space that typically isn't accounted for in the original design. It's also not wise to hang up too many things in a grow space, as they will eventually require maintenance and access can be challenging.

Getting air onto the leaves is critical for vapor pressure differential (VPD) control: the difference in absolute humidity (vapor pressure) in the air versus the internal vapor pressure of the leaf.

Ensuring the air around the plant is drier than the leaf structure encourages efficient transpiration, which allows better growth of the plant because transpiration is critical to nutrient delivery.

In order to maintain this differential, typically you need to adjust the RH. Lower RH will encourage more efficient transpiration. Controlling the VPD is calculated by the grow automation system, based on the room dew point as determined via a temperature sensor. Dew point is closely related to vapor pressure. The grow software can then send an RH setpoint to the HVAC system to ensure the required differential is met. Obviously, having an HVAC system that can communicate with your grow automation system is very important to have automatic and effective VPD control.

Any grower would be well-served by effective grow automation software that can tie all the systems together, so they work from common information, such as whether the lights are on or off, or if the plants are being watered, etc.

Automatic VPD control is done via the grow automation software, which can continuously tell your grow room HVAC to re-adjust its RH setpoint to better drive transpiration.

An important consideration is your type of ductwork. Make no mistake, you need to have a well-designed airflow distribution system; it is the only way to ensure complete air coverage.

Some have tried to simply hang their HVAC unit in the space with exposed inlets. This approach is poor for air distribution and will cause damage to your crop's health.

Instead, the duct system needs to be engineered and should meet requirements of the space for airflow and overall distribution pattern.

There is a trend to use fabric ducts because they are affordable and easy to take down for laundering between grow cycles. There are also now disposable ducts, which can simply be thrown out and replaced instead of cleaned and re-installed.

The ducts should have sufficient diameter to supply the required air. There is a tendency to select smaller ducts because they are cheaper and take up less space, but this puts more strain on the HVAC unit by increasing the external static pressure (ESP), forcing the fan to work harder, use more electricity, and be less effective. If you must use ducts with high ESP, the fans in the HVAC unit must be sized to force enough air through them to meet the demands of the space.

> External static pressure is the resistance to airflow caused by friction in air distribution networks. Lower resistance means less energy is needed to move air.

Additionally, it is not necessary to use filters above MerV-13 because higher-rated filters will impose a higher pressure drop, requiring more fan energy to push air through. In addition to the greater cost, there may not be an added benefit in particulate arrestance.

CONCLUSION

To determine the best growing conditions for your crop, you must first determine what you want and why. The conditions may vary depending on the intended final product, so it's very important to thoughtfully address what kind of requirements the environment needs to deliver on.

Knowing what lighting you'll use needs to be a first item on the to-do list, before you can get into HVAC selection. The choice of lighting type heavily influences HVAC loads, so your vendor cannot really suggest the proper solution without having all of the pertinent information. In Chapter 6, we provide a list that we at Agronomic IQ need to know before selecting equipment. Different vendors may have differing requirements.

When it comes to lighting, evidence supports providing cannabis plants with broader spectrum light than is currently the norm with metal-halide and HPS. Growers should be open to trying broad spectrum LED lighting for all stages of growth as it has the potential to improve yield and cannabinoid content, while also reducing operating costs. That said, it should be up to the grower based on their desired plant outcomes, as well as comfort level and trust, before choosing a lighting type.

As for the airside, it needs to be an engineered system that provides good airflow and high velocities to make the leaves dance. The idea is to prevent any stagnant air from forming around the leaves, as well as to provide warm air for the surface to encourage transpiration. Plants experience significant evaporative cooling due to transpiration, so they need to be supplied with lots of warm air to prevent condensation from forming on the leaf.

Vapor pressure differential control is critical to maximizing yield, as it makes the process more efficient and thus results in better delivery of nutrients within the plants. Controlling VPD is accomplished through the grow automation software, which monitors the room dew point and tells the HVAC unit when to adjust its RH setpoint.

HVAC SYSTEM TYPES

CHAPTER 08

Selecting the right HVAC system type for a grow room is crucial for the success of the crop. Adequate control over environmental conditions affects not only the health of the crop, but also energy consumption, and operating and maintenance costs.

Certain types of systems will cost the grower more to own and operate, which reduces the equipment's overall value and the owner's return on investment.

As discussed in Chapter 5: Navigating the Traditional Equipment Procurement Process, equipment value means a product that maximizes ROI by providing the best performance and the lowest overall cost (purchase, installation, operation, maintenance, and equipment longevity).

These costs are an important factor to control for many reasons. As noted in Chapter 6: Proper Sizing of HVAC, making prudent decisions about every element of the grow room is essential to maximizing profits and product quality. Selecting the HVAC system type is one of the most important elements to consider because of its potential impact on your budget and bottom line. There are different kinds of costs and their distinction is important. For example, sometimes purchase (capital/first) costs can be higher, but these are offset by a lower installation cost.

There is often a tendency to select equipment that provides the lowest first-cost. This choice may certainly save money at the front end, but often ends up costing even more to install and operate. For instance, it may be far more expensive to install comfort cooling with supplemental dehumidifiers, despite their capital cost being lower. Instead, the priority should be on the kind of equipment that will lead to lower operating costs. How? Choose energy-efficient solutions that will cost less to run in energy bills. Another important consideration is the kind of maintenance that will be required to keep the system in good operation for the long term. Certain kinds of equipment are easier and thus less expensive to maintain than others.

By looking at all the costs and factors that are related to a specific piece of equipment — and especially the HVAC system — you can determine an overall cost of ownership. Factors include the purchase price and installation cost of the equipment, as well as the long term cost of owning it, a period that could last 15–20 years for quality equipment. Only by reviewing the overall cost of ownership can you truly determine whether a specific piece of equipment provides good value.

FACTORS IN SELECTING AN HVAC SYSTEM

The health of the crop depends on having good control over environmental conditions, but there are also ramifications for energy consumption and capital, operating, and maintenance costs depending on the system that is chosen. All factors must be considered when selecting the HVAC system.

> Before making an equipment buying decision, factor in long term costs like annual maintenance requirements and how soon the equipment will need to be replaced.

To help the reader quickly understand the information in this chapter, each technology discussed will include this graphic to indicate the benefits and drawbacks of each system type.

Installed Cost	Operating Cost	Maintenance Costs	A/C Cooling	Dehumidification	Precision	Complexity	Scalability	Redundancy	Flexibility	Reliability	Plant Safety	Supplemental Dehumidification?
👍	👍	👍	👍	👎	👎	👎	👎	~	~	~	~	MAYBE

👍 Indicates a strength or net benefit to the grower.

👎 Indicates a weakness or net negative to the grower.

~ Indicates the potential to be designed as either a positive or a negative, and/or a neutral position.

EVALUATION CRITERIA

COST

Installed Cost — The comparative cost to hire a qualified firm to design, purchase equipment, properly install and commission the system.

Operating Cost — The comparative cost to operate the system to desired space conditions. This primarily consists of energy costs but should also consider hiring/training operators, any consumable components, and monitoring the equipment.

Maintenance Cost — The comparative costs to perform routine and annual preventative maintenance, as well as the anticipated costs of repair.

EFFICIENCY

Cooling — Ability of the system to adequately address the sensible cooling needs of the space in an energy-efficient manner.

Dehumidification — Ability of the system to adequately address the latent cooling (dehumidification) needs of the space in an energy-efficient manner without the need for supplemental dehumidification.

Precision — Ability of the system to hold a tight tolerance of the desired temperature/relative humidity conditions delivered to the room. (E.g. holding ± 1°F instead of ± 5°F)

DESIGN

Complexity — The level of complexity involved in the design, installation, and operation of this system. The higher the level of complexity, the more expensive it will be to hire the appropriate personnel to execute.

Scalability — Ability to easily and cost-effectively upgrade and expand the system as the facility grows to increase production.

Redundancy — The tendency for the system type to have redundant features, such as multiple cooling components, to provide back-up cooling if one component fails.

PRODUCTION/SAFETY

Operational flexibility — Ability of the system to satisfy a wide range of operational setpoints often required throughout the plant's lifetime. (e.g., 80°F/75% down to 60°F/40%)

Reliability — As typically installed, a combination of the expected lifetime and replacement costs for the HVAC system's components.

Plant Safety — Ability of the system to protect the plants from pathogens brought in from outside, pathogens recirculated within the facility, and other airborne risks, as well as potential system-related leaks in or around the grow rooms.

SUPPLEMENTAL DEHUMIDIFICATION

Supplemental Dehumidification — Some cooling technologies require supplementary dehumidification to meet the latent load. The technology typically used are standalone dehumidifiers hung in the space.

HVAC SYSTEM CATEGORIES

The three broad categories are:

- Custom air handlers with central refrigeration plant
- Air conditioning systems
- Dehumidifiers with heat rejection

Each category uses several different types of equipment but shares similarities in cost, operation, and primary function.

Custom Air Handlers with Central Refrigeration Plants are an engineering-intensive type of space conditioning systems that are built up from individual components that may come from one or many different manufacturers. Typically, a centralized space conditioning system uses chilled water as the energy transport medium, but other variations may use a refrigerant, such as ammonia. These systems are a tried-and-true solution for projects requiring large refrigeration capacity such as large commercial buildings, food processing facilities, and large campuses.

Air Conditioning Systems emerged as a solution geared towards grow facilities that were built by the owner or a trusted contractor without much input from design professionals. The air conditioning equipment could be off-the-shelf or custom order, but it rarely exceeds 25 tons of cooling capacity. As expected by the name, these systems are primarily focused on cooling the air to achieve the required setpoint temperature with dehumidification as a secondary effect. To compensate, additional latent removal capacity must be installed, usually in the form of standalone dehumidifiers.

Unitary Dehumidifiers with Heat Rejection originated from the world of swimming pool dehumidification, where a focus on a large latent load and a modest, sensible load mirrors the requirements of a grow room. The systems accomplish this with a unitary direct expansion (DX) dehumidifier that has reheat and outdoor heat rejection. This system offers the best of all worlds: maximum efficiency, the ability to cool and dehumidify (and easily switch between the two modes), low cost of ownership, flexibility, redundancy, and scalability.

The rest of this chapter explores these three system categories and the various technologies they represent.

DIFFERENCE BETWEEN AIR CONDITIONING AND DEHUMIDIFICATION

As a rule, air conditioners are designed to cool air to a desired temperature degree (comfort cooling or sensible cooling) but are not intended to address the absolute humidity content of the air. Dehumidifiers are purpose-built to reduce humidity levels via specific design elements not typically found in air conditioning equipment. Dehumidifiers, if equipped with heat rejection, can also provide comfort cooling.

CUSTOM AIR HANDLERS WITH CENTRAL REFRIGERATION PLANT

These large systems have three aspects in common: high installed costs, significant operational complexity, and the potential for extreme precision. They are designed by an engineering firm, composed of equipment from multiple manufacturers, installed by a professional contractor, and inspected/started by a commissioning agent. The system will be custom designed to provide the facility owner with the exact conditions required, but that precision comes at the premium of extreme complexity and high cost.

FOUR-PIPE CHILLED WATER SYSTEMS

Installed Cost	Operating Cost	Maintenance Costs	A/C Cooling	Dehumidification	Precision	Complexity	Scalability	Redundancy	Flexibility	Reliability	Plant Safety	Supplemental Dehumidification?
👎	~	👎	👍	👎	👍	👎	👎	~	👍	👍	👍	MAYBE

Typically found in facilities that require 1,000 tons or more of refrigeration capacity, such as large commercial buildings or even multiple buildings, chilled water systems are composed of a central mechanical plant holding the chillers and heat rejection (e.g., cooling towers). From the central plant, four pipes are run to the indoor grow rooms to provide: chilled water supply, chilled water return, warm water supply, and warm water return. The chilled water is used to provide both the sensible and, if properly designed, latent cooling. The warm water is to provide heat or reheat to the rooms in case they are overcooled during the dehumidification process, and the air must be warmed back up. Often, the warm water can be generated by heat recovery from the chiller's condenser water loop.

Chilled water systems, like the built-up refrigerant-based systems later described, are complex system designs that should only be used by those with extensive previous experience in the grow space. Improper design will lead to a very expensive system that will then require an equally expensive retrofit to meet the original project requirements.

COST

Installed Cost — These systems are heavily engineered, constructed to last 20 to 30 years, and use commercial grade materials. The installed cost will be quite high, because they incorporate many mechanical components and complex controls. Consideration for future expansion of the plant during the design phase will increase installation costs, otherwise scalability may not be possible.

Operating Cost — These systems can have some of the lowest energy costs for cooling; however, overall energy cost when including pump energy and auxiliary heating can approach or even exceed the costs of other technologies. The complexity will require skilled operators dedicated to the chilled water system.

Maintenance Cost — If the facility does not employ skilled technicians, the facility can expect frequent visits from a certified contractor. Many chiller manufacturers will not allow independent contractors to work on their equipment, which may further increase cost or delay repairs.

EFFICIENCY

Cooling — If designed properly, these systems will provide sufficient cooling to meet any indoor grow facility's needs.

Dehumidification — If designed properly, these systems will provide sufficient dehumidification to meet any indoor grow facility's needs. This requires that the chilled water temperature be at least 5–7°F below the desired space dew point, which can dramatically increase the energy costs of the chilled water plant. Additionally, this reduced water temperature may require reheat back to an acceptable level in order to provide a sufficient discharge air temperature into the space, further increasing energy footprint and/or system complexity.

Precision — If designed properly, these systems will hold a tight tolerance on temperature and relative humidity.

DESIGN

Complexity — The system is, by nature, very complex in design and operation.

Scalability — Since the heart of a chilled water system is one or more large chillers, it is not easily scalable unless the expansion was planned for and built into the original design. A scalable design on the central plant will be much more expensive to design and install.

Redundancy — Since the system is custom-designed, any level of redundancy is possible but will add considerable cost to the project. Redundancy is much more critical with a central plant design because failure of any part of the plant could affect the entire facility.

PRODUCTION/SAFETY

Operational flexibility — These systems can be designed to easily meet any operational setpoints desired for a room, or the system can be modified to meet the new specifications.

Reliability — Due to the industrial nature of the design, equipment, operation, and maintenance of this system, reliability is typically excellent. Beware, however, of ongoing maintenance needs and ensuring that the central plant — your building's single point of failure — is well maintained and operable.

Plant Safety — Since the system is custom-designed, any type of air filtration can be included in the design. A small refrigerant charge is maintained back in the chiller with water circulating around the facility, so there is little danger of a refrigerant leak harming the plants.

SUPPLEMENTAL DEHUMIDIFICATION

Supplemental Dehumidification — If properly designed, supplemental dehumidification will not be necessary.

SUMMARY

Four-pipe chilled water systems are the standard design for thousands of commercial buildings. Therefore, finding professionals with the capability to design, construct, and operate these facilities will be easy in a large, municipal area. The farther into rural areas the facility is built, the harder it will be to find qualified personnel to operate and maintain the system. If this type of system is chosen to condition your grow facility, be sure to work with the designer to lay out your operational expectations for the system both now and through future expansions.

Very few of these systems have been installed successfully in grow facilities as of the time this book was written. For that reason, even the most experience chilled water system designers have not refined the variation in the typical commercial building design to work properly for grow operations. In most applications we've seen, supplemental dehumidification has been added or a complete system redesign has been required to achieve the grower's specifications.

TWO-PIPE CHILLED WATER SYSTEMS

Installed Cost	Operating Cost	Maintenance Costs	A/C Cooling	Dehumidification	Precision	Complexity	Scalability	Redundancy	Flexibility	Reliability	Plant Safety	Supplemental Dehumidification?
👎	~	👎	👍	👎	👍	👎	👎	~	👍	👍	👍	YES

Like the four-pipe chilled water system, the two-pipe chilled water system is often composed of a central mechanical plant containing the chillers and heat rejection (e.g., cooling towers). To save capital costs, the chillers may also be air-cooled chillers that can be placed outside on a concrete pad. The use of air-cooled chillers will reduce the complexity and cost of the design but will also increase energy consumption and decrease the reliability and precision of the system.

From the chiller, only two pipes are run to the indoor grow rooms to provide chilled water supply and chilled water return. The reduction in piping removes the system's ability to provide heat/reheat through heat recovery from the chiller or a central boiler system. As there is no built-in reheat, either an auxiliary heat source would need to be provided so the chiller can run cold enough to dehumidify, or the chiller only provides air conditioning and supplemental dehumidification is required. The two-pipe system will still have nearly the same operational and maintenance complexity of the four-pipe system.

Again, a chilled water system is a complex system design that should only be designed by those with previous experience. Improper design will lead to a very expensive system that will then require an equally expensive retrofit to meet the original project requirements.

COST

Installed Cost — Because these systems are heavily engineered, constructed to last 20 to 30 years, and use commercial grade materials, the installed cost will be quite high. Consideration for future expansion of the plant, during design, will increase costs. The two-pipe design will have lower costs on the cooling side, but typically reheat or auxiliary heat will need to be provided remotely at an additional cost.

Operating Cost — If designed properly, these systems will have the lowest energy costs on the cooling side. The complexity, though, will require skilled operators dedicated to the chilled water system. The use of air-cooled over water-cooled chillers will increase the energy cost. The heating efficiency will depend on the type of heating system chosen. Chiller efficiency will be affected by water temperature; if the facility is hoping to have a dehumidification focus from chilled water, efficiency will significantly degrade.

Maintenance Cost — If the grower does not employ skilled technicians, they can expect frequent visits from a certified contractor. Many chiller manufacturers will not allow independent contractors to work on their equipment, which may further increase cost or delay repairs.

EFFICIENCY

Cooling — If designed properly, these systems will provide sufficient cooling to meet any indoor grow facility's needs.

Dehumidification — Two-pipe chilled water systems are typically design limited for dehumidification with a relatively warm chilled water temperature, but cooler water can add significant latent capacity. With this colder water, the facility will face the expense of needing dedicated reheat, affecting chiller efficiency. Typically, two-pipe chilled water systems are supplemented with standalone dehumidifiers.

Precision — If designed properly, these systems will hold a tight tolerance on temperature. The precision of the relative humidity control will be dependent upon the supplementary dehumidifiers or other system installed to provide latent removal.

DESIGN

Complexity — The system is, by nature, very complex in design and operation.

Scalability — Since the heart of a chilled water system is one or more large chillers, it is not easily scalable unless the expansion was planned for and built into the original design. A scalable design on the central plant will be much more expensive to design and install.

Redundancy — Since the system is custom-designed, any level of redundancy is possible but will add considerable cost to the project. Redundancy is much more critical with a central plant design as failure of any part of the plant could affect the entire facility.

PRODUCTION/SAFETY

Operational flexibility — These systems can be designed to meet any operational temperature setpoints desired for a room easily or the system can be modified to meet the new specifications. The flexibility of the relative humidity control will be dependent upon the supplementary dehumidifier or other system installed to provide latent removal.

Reliability — Due to the industrial nature of the design, equipment, operation, and maintenance of this system, reliability is often excellent for water-cooled chillers. Air-cooled chillers tend to be treated more like packaged rooftop units and have shorter expected lifetimes due to less expensive components and less frequent maintenance.

Plant Safety — Since the system is custom-designed, any type of air filtration can be included in the design. A small refrigerant charge is maintained back in the chiller with water circulating around the facility, so there is little danger of a refrigerant leak harming the plants.

SUPPLEMENTAL DEHUMIDIFICATION

Supplemental Dehumidification — Supplemental dehumidification will be necessary in most designs.

SUMMARY

Two-pipe chilled water systems are usually installed by those looking for the control of a chilled water system without the high price tag of a four-pipe system. However, the selection of this system without a proper design for supplemental heat and dehumidification may leave the grower quite disappointed. Once supplemental heating and/or dehumidification is added, the system cost approaches that of a four-pipe chilled water system, but only provides moderately better control than an air conditioning system. In every application of two-pipe systems we've seen, supplemental demodification or heating has been added.

> Two-pipe chillers may present a lower installed cost than a four-pipe chiller but will require the separate addition of a reheat source or supplementary dehumidification. When this is factored in, the cost differential narrows significantly.

BUILT-UP REFRIGERANT BASED SYSTEMS

Installed Cost	Operating Cost	Maintenance Costs	A/C Cooling	Dehumidification	Precision	Complexity	Scalability	Redundancy	Flexibility	Reliability	Plant Safety	Supplemental Dehumidification?
👎	~	👎	👍	👍	👍	👎	👎	~	👍	👍	~	NO

Very few indoor grow facilities have turned to industrial design firms to develop a built-up system such as the systems found in large food processing facilities, refrigerated warehouses, campus cooling systems, and other complex buildings with large refrigeration needs. These systems use a large central mechanical room to house the bulk of the compressors, vessels, and other components. The system then sends either the primary refrigerant (e.g., ammonia, CO_2) or a secondary refrigerant (e.g., chilled water, glycol, brine, CO_2) to deliver the cooling potential to the evaporators in the grow rooms. Separate provisions for auxiliary heat and/or reheat will need to be included with the system design. The design firms that develop these systems are experts at delivering to each room the exact conditions required. If you choose to construct a system like this, be certain the firms involved have prior experience with cannabis facilities.

> Due to the unique requirements of cannabis, make sure that any engineering firm bidding on a custom-designed plant system for your facility has had demonstrated success in a cannabis grow space. Success in an office building or college campus does not necessarily mean they are qualified to design a cannabis production system.

COST

Installed Cost — These systems are heavily engineered, constructed to last 25 to 50 years, and use industrial-grade materials. Therefore, the engineering and installation cost will be very high. Depending on the system design, there may be a hidden cost with adding supplementary heat to the systems. Most built-up refrigerant based systems are designed primarily for cooling and will therefore require an additional system for heat.

Operating Cost — If designed properly, these systems will incur amongst the lowest cooling energy costs. The complexity, though, will require skilled operators and possibly engineers on staff to manage regulatory requirements associated with such large systems. In addition, do not disregard the energy footprint of your auxiliary heating system.

Maintenance Cost — Since many of these systems use hazardous refrigerants (i.e., ammonia), the maintenance program will receive regulatory oversight by local and federal officials. If the facility does not include skilled technicians, they can expect frequent visits from a certified contractor.

EFFICIENCY

Cooling — If designed properly, these systems will provide sufficient cooling to meet any indoor grow facility's needs.

Dehumidification — If designed properly, these systems will provide sufficient dehumidification to meet any indoor grow facility's needs. Dehumidification will require the ability to add heat to a process air stream.

Precision — If designed properly, these systems will hold a tight tolerance on temperature and relative humidity.

DESIGN

Complexity — The system is, by nature, very complex in design and operation.

Scalability — These systems are typically designed to be easily scalable, but will require significant engineering design either included in the original design or subsequent re-design. Scalability adds cost.

Redundancy — Since the system is custom-designed, any level of redundancy is possible, although this will add considerable cost to the project. The use of hazardous refrigerants adds complexity to redundancy. Typically, each piece of a system will need to be inspected and certified, so adding more primary cooling/flow control devices/pressure vessels to the system to achieve greater redundancy will increase regulatory and maintenance costs.

PRODUCTION/SAFETY

Operational flexibility — These systems can be designed to easily meet any operational setpoints required for a room, or the system can be modified to meet the new specifications.

Reliability — Due to the industrial nature of the design, equipment, operation, and maintenance of this system, reliability is excellent if proper maintenance protocols are in place and facilities are managed by a professional plant operator.

Plant Safety — Since the system is custom-designed, any type of air filtration can be included in the design. Depending on how the system is designed, a refrigerant or other substance harmful to plants may be distributed throughout the facility, posing some risk in the event of a leak. Further, some of the industrial refrigerants used in this process — ammonia, for instance — are toxic to both plants and humans.

SUPPLEMENTAL DEHUMIDIFICATION

Supplemental Dehumidification — If properly designed, supplemental dehumidification will not be necessary.

SUMMARY

Built-up Refrigerant Based Systems can be custom designed to meet any environmental conditions required in an indoor grow facility. However, this level of precision and flexibility comes with a high price tag in both installed cost and personnel.

Distributed refrigerant systems using either CO_2 or ammonia introduce new hazards to a facility and may increase regulatory hurdles: CO_2 is an asphyxiant gas, and careful design must be able to quickly introduce outside air and lock out rooms that have suffered a catastrophic leak. These typically very large refrigerant charge systems introduce a new risk of frostbite or freezing and hazards associated with a leak in a way not typically found with the relatively small refrigerant charges of other air conditioning technologies.

Ammonia is highly toxic and has been involved in several industrial accidents as a result of a lack of maintenance or proper safety protocols. Regulatory and approval hurdles will be in place, as well as the potential need for evacuation protocols for a large area around a facility with an ammonia-based plant.

For these reasons, very few indoor grow facilities even consider this system as an option.

AIR CONDITIONING SYSTEMS

These systems typically use off the shelf equipment designed to cool residential and light commercial facilities to provide cooling to the grow facility. The equipment may have a lower first cost, easier installation, simple operation, and a 10–15 year expected lifetime. Servicing the equipment is quite easy due to its prevalence in the commercial building market in both urban and rural areas.

Most equipment in this category is designed around cooling with dehumidification as a benefit of the cold coil but not necessarily the focus of the design. To offset this gap, the addition of supplemental dehumidification capacity is essential. Supplemental heating capacity may also be required.

While the individual pieces of equipment are inexpensive, the overall system can become quite costly to install and operate. A large facility might have dozens of air conditioners, supplemental heaters, and supplemental dehumidifiers. Each piece of equipment will require an electrical connection, a plumbing connection for condensate, and physical installation. There is a cost associated with each of the tasks required to install every individual unit, so fewer total units will generally cost less. Additionally, there will be costs associated with maintaining every single unit. All of these additional units, however, can increase redundancy within the space.

There will be a short discussion of supplemental dehumidifiers at the end of this section. Supplemental dehumidifiers are considered standalone, self-contained dehumidification units that can be simply hung in the space with no additional ductwork required, but will require plumbing to remove condensate. They work with the air conditioning system to remove moisture from the space during the "lights on" period and carry the bulk of the dehumidification load during the "lights out" period when the heat load drops off and air conditioning systems tend not to operate.

SPLIT SYSTEM AIR CONDITIONERS

Installed Cost	Operating Cost	Maintenance Costs	A/C Cooling	Dehumidification	Precision	Complexity	Scalability	Redundancy	Flexibility	Reliability	Plant Safety	Supplemental Dehumidification?
👍	~	👍	👍	👎	~	👍	👍	~	~	~	~	YES

These air conditioning systems are quite similar to the "central A/C" units found in single-family homes across North America. The system consists of a condensing unit (i.e., compressor and condenser) placed outside. From the condensing units, two copper lines carry refrigerant to and from an evaporator located inside the building, usually inside an air handler or above a furnace. The condensing unit can be placed on an outside pad, suspended from the side of the building, or on the roof. Do not confuse this with a "rooftop unit," which is a packaged air conditioner that delivers air to the facility. This unit will be discussed later in this section.

From the aspect of cooling, the units can be very energy efficient, the operation is simple on/off, and due to their small size, it will be necessary to install multiple units, thus providing redundancy. Installation and servicing of the units can be performed by any licensed HVAC contractor. If the unit installed is a heat pump, it is possible to obtain heat from the unit, although installing inexpensive supplemental heating is usually a better choice.

Dehumidification of the air is not the focus of split system air conditioners. Typically, only 10% to 20% of the coil's cooling capacity is used for the latent load. In fact, as the efficiency of split systems increases, it usually means the system has been modified to focus more on sensible (i.e., air temperature) reduction and less on dehumidification. During the "lights out" period, when there is very little heat load, a split system will barely run since it does not have reheat capabilities. With virtually no "lights out" dehumidification capability, supplemental dehumidifiers must be included.

The evaporators for split system air conditioners can be placed nearly anywhere in the facility, which allows for considerable flexibility in facility design.

Cooling during low-ambient conditions (i.e., winter) is a concern with a split system. Most air conditioners are designed with the assumption they will not be needed when it's cooler than 60°F outside (about 15°C). But the grow space, due to heat from the lights, has a continuous requirement for cooling throughout the year.

COST

Installed Cost — These systems are mass-produced for the residential and commercial markets and can be installed by any licensed HVAC technician. The installed cost will be quite low.

Operating Cost — If designed and installed properly, the cost for cooling the air could be within an acceptable range. However, too often, excess capacity is installed, and the operational efficiency is degraded by multiple units turning on and off. The additional energy consumption (and space heat gain) due to supplemental dehumidification should be included in any comparison, so be certain to install the highest efficiency dehumidifiers possible.

Maintenance Cost — Like a residential air conditioner, the maintenance cost of these units for the first few years should be minimal. As they age, the maintenance and/or replacement cost will rise. Most split system air conditioners are built with an expected lifetime of 10 years under moderate use.

EFFICIENCY

Cooling — If designed properly, these systems will provide sufficient cooling to meet any indoor grow facility's needs. The higher-end split systems can rival the efficiency of chilled water systems, but the equipment cost will be prohibitive.

Dehumidification — Split system air conditioners are built to provide sensible cooling without a significant focus on dehumidification. Supplemental dehumidifiers will be necessary.

Precision — A single split system air conditioner cannot vary its capacity to hold a tight temperature tolerance. Since most grow facilities will have multiple units installed, the coordinated operation of multiple units can improve the precision but still not to the same level as a more complex system.

DESIGN

Complexity — The system is, by nature, very simple in design and operation.

Scalability — Because these systems are essentially several individual small systems, they are easily scalable by simply adding more split systems to an expanded grow facility.

Redundancy — Because these systems are essentially several individual small systems, the level of redundancy is quite high.

PRODUCTION/SAFETY

Operational flexibility — A single split system's operation is restricted to a simple on/off scenario. When multiple units are installed, and air handlers are upgraded to variable speed fans, more operational flexibility can be obtained.

Reliability — Each split system would be considered low on the reliability scale, but due to redundancy inherent in a design with multiple split systems, it can be reasonably assured that at least some cooling will be available to the facility at all times.

Plant Safety — Split systems contain a large volume of refrigerant compared to the cooling capacity provided due to the need to send refrigerant back and forth between the evaporator and condensing unit. If there were a catastrophic leak, the loss of this refrigerant might harm or possibly kill plants. Since the air handler portion of a split system is often custom designed, nearly any type of air filtration can be included in the design.

SUPPLEMENTAL DEHUMIDIFICATION

Supplemental Dehumidification — Supplemental dehumidification will be necessary. Be certain to choose the most energy efficient dehumidifier possible to reduce the heat load on the space.

SUMMARY

Split system air conditioners are often the least expensive method to provide a system for cooling grow operations. With proper selection, design, and installation, a split system air conditioner can provide adequate, reliable, and efficient cooling of a grow facility with easy operation and scalability.

However, this system cannot provide adequate dehumidification for a grow facility. Either excess cooling capacity with reheat, or supplemental dehumidification capacity, must be installed. High-efficiency standalone dehumidifiers are always recommended over reheat to meet building energy regulations and reduce energy consumption. Standalone dehumidifiers will also be required to handle the "lights out" latent load.

This system selection is quite prevalent in the grow industry primarily because it is often the lowest first-cost option that can be installed by any contractor without the use of a design professional. Therefore, it has become the system of choice for many growers. As these growers expand into larger facilities, split systems rarely remain their system of choice due to the limited operational flexibility, high maintenance cost, and hassle of the units as they age.

PACKAGED AIR CONDITIONER

Installed Cost	Operating Cost	Maintenance Costs	A/C Cooling	Dehumidification	Precision	Complexity	Scalability	Redundancy	Flexibility	Reliability	Plant Safety	Supplemental Dehumidification?
👍	~	👍	👍	👎	~	👍	👍	~	~	~	~	YES

Packaged air conditioning units are known by many names, including rooftop packages, rooftop units, unitary A/C, "all-in-one" packages, and many more. Many of the names are descriptive of their location (i.e., rooftop) or their functions (e.g., all-in-one). Depending on the features paid for in a packaged A/C, a single unit could be able to provide any air treatment desired by a grower.

Packaged A/C units have a single cabinet that pulls air from the facility, mixes in the required amount of outside air (if applicable), and delivers the air back to the space at the required temperature and filtration levels. Packaged A/C performs all this by placing a direct expansion air conditioning system, a method of reheating the air, and filtration inside a single box. The price of the unit grows quickly with each additional feature.

While these units can be purchased in the same size as a split system air conditioner, they are often installed in capacities two to four times larger. The smaller units do not have enough space in the physical box to offer all of the features growers look for in a packaged A/C unit.

A packaged A/C unit will always have a direct expansion air conditioning unit. Like split systems, the efficiency can range from code minimum to very efficient, but as the efficiency increases, the cost increases, and the dehumidification capability tends to decrease. The packaged A/C unit will most likely have a natural gas/propane furnace installed that is minimum efficiency and basic filtration to protect the coils.

On the high end of packaged A/C units, the unit can include heat recovery, humidification, advanced filtration (e.g., high MERV filters, UV light), variable speed compressors, variable speed blowers, and dehumidification. Dehumidification capability is included by splitting the refrigeration system in the packaged A/C into two circuits. One circuit will reject heat outside like normal. The second circuit will have a second condenser coil in the conditioned air stream. In this way, the air is cooled by the evaporator and then reheated using heat recovered from the refrigeration system, just like a standalone dehumidifier. The grow room industry often refers to this system as an "all-in-one" unit. When considering this option, be sure to evaluate both the first-costs of adding the coil and the operating costs. The addition of the single condenser coil can increase the equipment cost of a packaged A/C unit by up to one-third, and the efficiency in dehumidification mode is one-half to one-quarter that of an efficient standalone dehumidifier.

Like split systems, cooling during low-ambient conditions (i.e., winter) is a concern with a packaged A/C unit. Most air conditioners are designed with the assumption they will not be needed when it's cooler than 60°F outside (about 15°C). But the grow space, due to heat from the lights, has a continuous requirement for cooling throughout the year. They often compensate for this by running in "economizer" mode, which means bringing in outside air to provide the cooling instead of running the compressor. If your operation runs elevated

CO_2 levels, this will dilute those levels back to ambient. Be sure to discuss this point with your design professionals and contractors when selecting equipment.

COST

Installed Cost — These systems are mass-produced for the residential and commercial markets and can be installed by any licensed HVAC technician. The installed cost will be low to moderate, depending on its location and the structural support required.

Operating Cost — If designed and installed properly, the cost for cooling the air could be within an acceptable range. However, too often, excess capacity is installed, and the operational efficiency is degraded by multiple units turning on and off. The additional energy consumption of supplemental dehumidification should be included in any comparison, therefore be certain to install the highest efficiency dehumidifiers possible.

Maintenance Cost — Like a residential air conditioner, the maintenance cost of these units for the first few years should be minimal. As they age, the maintenance and/or replacement cost will rise. Most packaged air conditioners are built with an expected lifetime of 10 years under moderate use.

EFFICIENCY

Cooling — If designed properly, these systems will provide sufficient cooling to meet any indoor grow facility's needs. The higher-end packaged A/C units can rival the efficiency of chilled water systems, but the equipment cost will be prohibitive.

Dehumidification — Packaged air conditioners are built to provide sensible cooling without a significant focus on dehumidification. By adding a condensing coil to the process air stream, sufficient dehumidification capacity can be obtained, but be sure to compare the first-cost and operating efficiency to that of supplemental dehumidifiers. Often, it is cheaper to install and operate high-efficiency standalone dehumidifiers.

Precision — A packaged air conditioner cannot vary its capacity to hold a tight temperature tolerance unless variable speed fans and compressors are purchased. Since most grow facilities will have multiple units installed, the coordinated operation of multiple units can improve the precision but still not to the same level as a more complex system.

DESIGN

Complexity — The system is, by nature, very simple in design and operation, but the complexity will increase as features are added to the packaged air conditioner.

Scalability — Since the system is self-contained, it is easy to scale up by adding more packaged air conditioning units to an expanded grow facility.

Redundancy — If multiple packaged air conditioners are used to cool a single room, some level of redundancy is available.

PRODUCTION/SAFETY

Operational flexibility — Most packaged air conditioners' operation is restricted to a simple on/off scenario. To obtain more operational flexibility, either multiple units need to be installed, or variable speed fans and compressors must be used.

Reliability — Depending on the initial price point of the packaged air conditioning system, they can be considered reliable for the warranty period with proper maintenance, but the expected lifetime is 10 to 15 years under moderate use.

Plant Safety — The refrigerant charge in a packaged air conditioner is so minimal that a catastrophic loss will have minimal impact on the plants. If the unit is large enough, nearly any type of air filtration can be included in the design or placed external to the air conditioner.

SUPPLEMENTAL DEHUMIDIFICATION

Supplemental Dehumidification — Larger packaged air conditioners can offer the option of a condenser coil in the process air stream to provide proper dehumidification capacity. When considering this option, be sure to evaluate both the first-cost of adding the coil and the operating costs. The addition of the single condenser coil can increase the equipment cost of the packaged A/C unit by up to one-third, and the efficiency in dehumidification mode is one-half to one-quarter of an efficient standalone dehumidifier.

SUMMARY

Growers often install packaged air conditioners because the first-cost of stripped-down units will be only slightly higher than the split systems previously mentioned. With proper selection, design, and installation, they can provide adequate, reliable, and efficient cooling of a grow facility with easy operation and scalability. If the budget exists for an upgraded system, the units can also be outfitted to provide advanced filtration and some dehumidification to the facility.

If selecting this piece of equipment, be certain to understand each feature, what it will cost, and the performance it will deliver to your facility's operating conditions. Before meeting with a contractor or equipment dealer, write down the operating conditions and other important features for each stage of the plant's growth cycle. Be certain the packaged air conditioner can meet your desired conditions at all times, including during the "lights out" period when sensible cooling loads fall off, as well as during low-ambient conditions.

If you are considering using a packaged air conditioning system as a dehumidifier by adding an extra condensing coil to the airstream, examine the added cost of the coil and the operational efficiency in dehumidification mode. Comparing this cost to the addition of supplemental dehumidifiers often turns facility owners away from this option.

Do not disregard the cost of preparing a location for the packaged air conditioner as part of the installation costs. If placed outside, a reinforced concrete pad is usually required. If placed on the roof, the facility will need to be able to support it structurally. If placed inside, a means for moving air to and from the condenser is required to reject heat from the facility.

VARIABLE REFRIGERANT FLOW (VRF) MULTI-SPLIT AIR CONDITIONERS

Installed Cost	Operating Cost	Maintenance Costs	A/C Cooling	Dehumidification	Precision	Complexity	Scalability	Redundancy	Flexibility	Reliability	Plant Safety	Supplemental Dehumidification?
👍	~	~	👍	👎	~	~	~	~	~	~	~	YES

Variable refrigerant flow multi-split air conditioners (VRF) are a built-up system of specially made split system air conditioners. A VRF system will consist of one or more condensing units and possibly dozens of evaporators all sharing the same refrigerant loop. The VRF system is assembled from off-the-shelf components, but the configuration is always unique and usually developed by an HVAC design professional. These systems are also referred to as Variable Refrigerant Volume (VRV) systems.

VRF systems come in three basic forms: cooling only, heat pump, and heat recovery. In cooling only mode, each evaporator can only provide cooling to the space it serves. In heat pump mode, each evaporator provides heating or cooling to each space depending upon what the thermostat is asking. Heat recovery mode is similar to heat pump mode, except the heat pulled out of a room calling for cooling can be moved to a room calling for heat, thus increasing the overall efficiency of the system.

The ventilation needs of the space are often decoupled from the VRF system, which means if outside air is needed for the space to dilute the indoor air, it must be brought in and conditioned by a separate system. Since many grow operations try to maintain elevated CO_2 levels, this can be considered beneficial.

The true value in a VRF system is installing it in the heat recovery mode so that energy can be conserved, but this only works when there are simultaneous heating and cooling loads. Since grow operations are cooling dominated, this feature offers little benefit for the bulk of the year unless simultaneous heating and cooling loads can be established for a single facility/ system. The cooling only VRF systems offer only marginally better efficiency than standard split system air conditioners.

Manufacturers of VRF systems vary on their claims of dehumidification capability. Most evaporators are designed for offices and other commercial buildings. They are commonly called fan coil units or cassettes and have poor latent removal capacity. To offset this, many VRF manufacturers have designed special evaporators with higher latent capacity specifically to handle the large latent load of outside air.

If properly designed, a VRF system with the high latent removal evaporators can provide most of the dehumidification capacity needed when the space is in cooling mode. If there is a reduced cooling load, like during "lights out," reheat is necessary. The system also needs to be accurately sized to match the cooling load. Otherwise, the evaporators will not run long enough to achieve full dehumidification potential. Since systems are often oversized, it has been our experience that supplemental dehumidification is frequently added to VRF system installations.

Due to the large refrigerant volume contained in a VRF system, precautions must be taken to meet building safety codes (e.g., International Building Code, ASHRAE Standard 15). If there is a catastrophic loss of refrigerant in a single room, the occupants of that room could be asphyxiated by the refrigerant. While there has been little research on the effects of refrigerant on plant tissues, it is presumed the effects would be detrimental.

Like split systems, cooling during low-ambient conditions (i.e., winter) is a concern with a VRF system. Be sure the system is equipped to run when it's cooler than 60°F outside (about 15°C).

COST

Installed Cost — The VRF components are mass-produced for the residential and commercial markets but should be designed and installed by certified professionals. The installed cost will be moderate to high depending on the complexity of the design.

Operating Cost — If designed and installed properly, the cost for cooling the air will be within an acceptable range and better than the other air conditioning equipment in this section. Too often, excess capacity is installed, and the operational efficiency is degraded by multiple units turning on and off. The addition of energy consumption of supplemental dehumidification should be included in any comparison, so be certain to install the highest efficiency dehumidifiers possible.

Maintenance Cost — Like a residential air conditioner, the maintenance cost of these units for the first few years should be minimal. As they age, the maintenance and/or replacement cost will rise. Most VRF components are built with an expected lifetime of 10 years under moderate use.

EFFICIENCY

Cooling — If designed properly, these systems will provide sufficient cooling to meet any indoor grow facility's needs. If the heat recovery VRF version can be used, the total efficiency of the system can be substantial.

Dehumidification — As previously mentioned, some manufacturers have evaporators that can provide adequate dehumidification capability when the air conditioning is needed. During "lights out" times, reheat will be needed. This reheat could be from supplemental sources or by running some of the evaporators in heating mode if a reheat system was installed. Often it is cheaper to install and operate high-efficiency standalone dehumidifiers.

Precision — A VRF air conditioner system could hold a tight temperature tolerance with proper component selection and design. Holding to tight tolerances on the dehumidification load will be more difficult unless supplemental dehumidification is also installed.

DESIGN

Complexity — The system is, by nature, complex in design and operation. The complexity will increase as features are added to provide additional control and energy-saving features.

Scalability — If initially designed with future expansion in mind, the system can be easily scalable. Otherwise, the expansion of an existing system may be difficult.

Redundancy — With the need for multiple evaporators in the space, there is considerable redundancy of the individual components. If there is a failure in the controls, refrigerant loop, or other shared portion of the system, the entire system will be down until that portion is repaired.

PRODUCTION/SAFETY

Operational flexibility — VRF systems modulate refrigerant flow and use variable-speed compressors, allowing great flexibility in operation. As mentioned previously, they are able to hold a precise temperature. A single condensing unit can be connected to multiple indoor evaporators of differing capacities, although relying on one condenser could threaten redundancy efforts.

Reliability — Depending on the initial price point of the VRF system, they can be considered reliable for the warranty period with proper maintenance. The typical expected lifetime is about 18–20 years under moderate use.

Plant Safety — The refrigerant charge in VRF systems is very large and a leak could be hazardous for plants. VRF systems are often ductless so a separate ventilation system must be designed, which could be equipped with nearly any type of air filtration desired.

SUPPLEMENTAL DEHUMIDIFICATION

Supplemental Dehumidification — While VRF systems can be equipped with evaporators that provide latent capacity, they will typically not have reheat capability and, as a result, can only supplement dehumidification when there is a simultaneous call for cooling. It is more typical to see VRF systems paired with standalone dehumidifiers.

SUMMARY

Growers often install VRF because the first-cost of stripped-down units will be only slightly higher than the split systems previously mentioned. With proper selection, design, and installation, they can provide adequate, reliable, and efficient cooling of a grow facility with easy operation and scalability. If the budget exists for an upgraded system, the units can also be outfitted to provide advanced filtration and some dehumidification to the facility.

If selecting this piece of equipment, be certain to understand each feature, what it will cost, and the performance it will deliver to your facility's operating conditions. Before meeting with a contractor or equipment dealer, write down the operating conditions and other important features for each stage of the plant's growth cycle. Be certain the VRF system can meet your desired conditions at all times, including during the "lights out" period when cooling loads fall off.

If you are considering using a VRF system with latent-capacity evaporators, consider the added cost and what the efficiency of the system will be, then compare to the addition of high-efficiency supplemental dehumidifiers.

STANDALONE DEHUMIDIFIERS

Installed Cost	Operating Cost	Maintenance Costs	A/C Cooling	Dehumidification	Precision	Complexity	Scalability	Redundancy	Flexibility	Reliability	Plant Safety	Supplemental Dehumidification?
👍	~	👍	👎	👍	~	👍	👍	~	👍	~	~	NO

These dehumidification systems are functionally similar to a small plug-in dehumidifier that you might find in the average residential basement, and in the infancy of the industry, may actually have been exactly the same. These days, such dehumidifiers are more likely to be offered at industrial voltages and at much higher capacities. They operate with a simple refrigeration system consisting of, at minimum, an evaporator coil to cool and dry the air, and a hot gas reheat coil to reject the heat of compression plus energy taken from the air in dehumidifying, into the supply airstream.

Their elegance is their portability and ease of installation: many portable units have wheels to allow for easy movement between rooms. This would allow, for instance, a grower to move a portable dehumidifier between several drying rooms to supplement a particular room during the first 24 hours of a drying cycle. As well, they are often equipped with 120V or 240V standard plugs.

Others, at the behest of growers, are designed to be hung in a grow space to supplement the dehumidification capacity of an air conditioning system. Many units (two at a minimum, but often four to eight) are used in a single room to provide distributed capacity, mitigate microclimates within the space, and provide redundancy. There is a cost, however; each unit will need to be provided with some structure to hang it from the roof, an electrical connection, and a condensate drain, requiring the coordination of mechanical, electrical, and plumbing trades for installation.

Control of the units vary from a simple humidistat on the portable unit to a wall mounted low voltage controller or even an activation signal received from a grow automation system controlling the balance of the room. Again, there are trade-offs: unit-mounted humidistat controls will be the least accurate but cheapest and simplest to operate. Integration with grow automation comes at an installation cost but will allow for coordination of all units in a space and much more accurate control.

Differences between manufacturers typically center around product quality, control strategies, and efficiencies. The more efficient a system, the more work (in this case, moisture removal) you'll get for a given electrical cost, an obvious benefit. The hidden benefit, most often overlooked, is that more efficient units will deliver less heat to the space. Because grow rooms are cooling dominant rooms, there is a double efficiency gain by not causing additional strain on the sensible cooling system in a space.

COST

Installed Cost — These systems are mass-produced and readily available. The installation cost will vary from next to nothing — the cost of unpacking and plugging in a unit — to moderate if new electrical, plumbing, and hanging supports need to be added.

Operating Cost — Operating cost is directly tied to the efficiency of the unit. Don't forget the hidden cost of inefficient dehumidifiers on additional load to your cooling system.

Maintenance Cost — Like a basement dehumidifier, maintenance is very minimal. Some will have permanent filters that will need to be washed on a regular interval, whereas others will use disposable filters that will need to be replaced, typically between each grow cycle. Ensure ease of access to reduce maintenance time and expense.

EFFICIENCY

Cooling — These systems add sensible heat to the space and therefore reduce cooling efficiency. Your cooling system needs to be sized for this heat gain.

Dehumidification — Designed specifically for this purpose, supplemental dehumidifiers are among the most efficient methods for removing moisture from air. That said, efficiencies vary from code minimum to over eight pints/kWh. Higher efficiency will provide more effective dehumidification with lower costs.

Precision — Individual units are unable to maintain tight control of space relative humidity, but as spaces acquire more units and a better distributed dehumidification capacity, the space will average much closer to setpoint. Setpoint accuracy will be determined by control type, as mentioned in the introduction to this system type.

DESIGN

Complexity — The system is, by nature, very simple in design and operation.

Scalability — As these units are essentially several small, individual systems, they are easily scalable by simply adding more. Remember that as you add more dehumidifiers to a space, you're increasing sensible heat and therefore may also need to add supplemental cooling, although the heat these units create is often beneficial during "lights off."

Redundancy — As these systems are essentially several individual small systems, the level of redundancy is quite high.

PRODUCTION/SAFETY

Operational flexibility — A single dehumidifier's operation is restricted to a simple on/off scenario. When multiple units are installed, more operational flexibility in operating conditions can be obtained. The ability to move portable units to rooms requiring immediate supplemental dehumidification allows for operational flexibility.

Reliability — When there are multiple units in a room, redundancy is easily achieved and thus the overall system will be reliable. Individual product reliability varies by manufacturer (you often get what you pay for.) Some domestically manufactured products come with a five-year warranty, are of higher quality, and offer product replacement when needed. Most imports come with one-year warranty, would be considered low on the reliability scale, and lack product support.

Plant Safety — Portable dehumidifiers generally contain relatively small amounts of refrigerant, likely below the threshold that would be damaging to plants or hazardous to operators. There is a risk of a single unit failing and losing control of space relative humidity, but this single failure is easily mitigated with redundancy.

SUPPLEMENTAL DEHUMIDIFICATION

Supplemental Dehumidification — Dehumidifiers are designed to provide the full latent cooling requirements of a space or to supplement existing capacity. No other technology of dehumidification will be required to supplement them.

SUMMARY

Standalone dehumidifiers are an easy, relatively inexpensive and potentially very efficient way to meet the dehumidification demands of your grow facility or to supplement the latent heat removal provided by existing cooling systems. All grow facilities require the ability to remove moisture during both lights on and lights off operation, as well as during drying of harvested product, so their use is both ubiquitous and necessary.

Growers can take advantage of increasingly more efficient technologies that both increase moisture removal and decrease energy use. Standalone dehumidifiers have been historically limited to about 500 pints per day but are now commercially available at capacities of more than 800 pints per day. Efficiency comes at the expense of higher capital cost and a larger equipment size, but payback is often within a year or less, especially if you consider the expense of cooling rejected heat.

Many growers will even have "stand by" units available to provide supplemental capacity in rooms that are at particular stages of growth or that have seen a failure in another mechanical system. Typically, standalone dehumidifiers are a prudent investment.

UNITARY DEHUMIDIFIERS WITH HEAT REJECTION

Installed Cost	Operating Cost	Maintenance Costs	A/C Cooling	Dehumidification	Precision	Complexity	Scalability	Redundancy	Flexibility	Reliability	Plant Safety	Supplemental Dehumidification?
~	👍	~	👍	👍	👍	👍	👍	~	👍	~	~	NO

Unitary dehumidifiers evolved mainly from equipment manufactured for conditioning indoor pool environments. The two applications (grow rooms and indoor pools) are closely related by their similar latent load requirements coupled with a moderate sensible demand. These units incorporate design elements not found in standard air conditioners to provide better ability to dehumidify and/or cool air, and easily modulate between the two modes. Unlike standalone dehumidifiers, they use remote or packaged outdoor heat rejection to maintain interior space temperature.

Unitary dehumidification systems of this nature are designed to be a full solution to grow room space demands by offering heating, cooling, and dehumidification in a single package. They provide energy-efficient sensible cooling as a natural by-product of the dehumidification process, where air is cooled to below its dew point. When reheat capability is included, the same air can be used to provide air conditioning.

There is a risk with unitary designs of over-drying the space because they are designed with a latent focus and only provide cooling as a by-product of the dehumidification. However, they can avoid this problem. Unlike standalone dehumidifiers, which cannot provide cooling, or certain air conditioners that provide limited dehumidification, unitary equipment can avoid over-drying the space, provided that reheat capability is included to ensure the air isn't too cold.

This feature introduces the risk of over-drying the space when the lights are on and a sensible heat load is being added to the room. This is because the coils are designed with a latent focus and sensible cooling is provided as a by-product of dehumidification.

However, certain modern equipment designs now include variable-capacity compressors that can stage performance to provide either temperature control with no dehumidification, or full dehumidification with the potential for temperature control. With the unitary design, the grower can have full environment control out of one unit.

If the dehumidification equipment is not designed with this variable capacity feature, then it may be necessary to artificially humidify the space, which would carry its own costs and reduce the facility's overall energy efficiency.

Some manufacturers have combined variable-capacity compressors with airflow modulation to ensure their capability of both cooling and dehumidification closely matches the space requirements, further driving energy efficiency while providing more stable space conditions.

Conventional unitary designs use hot gas reheat, which operates through an on/off valve to control the reheat coil. In other words, you either have no heat, or you have all the heat. On/off reheat causes temperature and RH swings in the space. When it's on, the temperature drives up, which also drives the RH down. Eventually it overheats the space, so it goes off and air conditioning is activated. This cools the space, driving the temperature down and the RH back up. It then over-cools and the process is repeated.

The frequent bouncing between hot and cold temperatures places considerable strain on the equipment and risks crop health. Also, it's not good for equipment longevity and is very inefficient in terms of energy usage.

Some new equipment designs avoid this instability by modulating reheat through a control algorithm that bleeds as much or as little heat necessary to the outdoors to keep the space temperature stable, 24/7. As a result, the RH is also kept as stable as possible.

> Maintaining stable temperature and RH levels in a grow space is critical. Unitary dehumidifiers that use modulating reheat are a reliable way to avoid wide swings in temperature and RH.

There are two main ways to bleed heat outdoors.

It's important to pick the right method of modulating reheat, because grow rooms are unusual in the fact that they require significant air conditioning year-round, regardless of exterior temperatures.

As with both split air conditioning systems and packaged A/C units, there is a risk of reduced performance or reliability at low ambient conditions (cold weather).

The traditional method is via the split-DX approach, where the dehumidifier runs a refrigeration circuit to an outside air-cooled condenser (OACC). This traditional set-up is common in the dehumidification industry, but it is highly problematic for grow rooms, and growers and engineers should be aware of the issues.

One of the problems with some split-DX system designs is the tremendous refrigerant liability these systems pose. Because they use a very large circuit, they can use hundreds of pounds of refrigerant. Not only is this expensive to initially charge or to replace if there's ever a leak, it's also potentially harmful because refrigerant is toxic to plants. Refrigerants, like R-410A — commonly used in HVAC — also pose an environmental risk because of high global warming potential (GWP) if released into the atmosphere.

R-410A is going to be phased out in the next few years. Any system sold today that uses it will see a phase-out during its lifetime and, unfortunately, refrigerant is not interchangeable in specific refrigeration systems. As when R-22 was phased out, the prices for R-410A will probably rise significantly over time. As a dehumidifier ages, it becomes more likely to suffer a leak. Thus, a grower buying a system with a large R-410A charge today may face thousands of dollars in replacement costs several years down the road if their system suffers a leak when refrigerant prices are higher.

Especially in cooler climates, oil and refrigerant migration are a concern. Split-DX systems suffer this problem when air conditioning mode is turned off, either briefly or for long periods of time in the winter. When the OACC is off, the oil and refrigerant present in the system are drawn by cold temperatures and migrate to the outdoor condenser.

Typical problems with the split-DX approach include large refrigerant charges, increased chances of compressor slugging and flooding, as well as higher installation and maintenance costs. All of these can be a liability for growers, but are avoidable by selecting a water-cooled system.

When air conditioning mode is turned back on, the liquid mix is quickly recalled and slams into the circuit, causing premature wear. On large systems, it often leads to compressor failure, thus requiring expensive repairs and equipment downtime.

These problems are, in fact, common complaints in the dehumidification industry whenever traditional split-DX equipment is applied. Yet the grow room industry is having to deal with them as well because it's a common and cheap solution, with little thought given to whether it is the best solution.

So, what is the better way?

The better way to set up a DX system would be to use a split water-cooled system, such as a dry cooler, cooling tower, adiabatic cooler, or geothermal loop. In this set-up, refrigerant is kept inside the dehumidifier in a circuit sealed at the factory. Outside the unit, it's only water, with glycol used to prevent freezing. For some of these solutions, the owner only needs a plumber to hook it up on installation, not an expensive certified refrigeration technician. PVC piping can be used instead of copper.

The small refrigeration circuit cuts refrigerant requirements from 50% to more than 80%, which is a significant saving in charging costs and a major reduction in environmental liability.

Water-cooled systems also do not need refrigerant adjustments like traditional split-DX outdoor condensers require. Facilities with traditional outdoor condensers need to open them up twice a year, in the winter and summer, to match the refrigerant inside to the outdoor conditions. This is a maintenance pain point for many facilities.

With water-cooled devices, not only are refrigerant and oil migration problems eliminated, but you also do not have a limit on line-set length. By comparison, condensers using refrigerant can typically only be placed a maximum of 50 feet away, which is too short a distance to work in many installations, so engineers try to push it farther. But the longer the line is, the more strain is placed on the compressor.

Many headaches can be avoided by using water-cooled heat rejection for DX systems, but they are not commonly employed by the industry because many engineers and growers are not aware of all the problems they solve. Part of the reason for this skepticism is that they are expensive for manufacturers to provide, and that cost is passed onto the buyer.

The slightly higher purchase cost of a water cooled DX system is more than offset by a lower installation cost, overall cost of ownership, and vastly reduced operating and maintenance hassles.

COST

Installed Cost — A system will have a balanced installed cost: the equipment is more expensive to buy, but the installation and integration is simple as there are typically only one or two units per grow space, reducing the complexity of work and number of electrical, plumbing, and mechanical connections required. This reduced complexity also translates to faster installation. Additionally, use of PVC piping for some methods of outdoor heat rejection (such as dry coolers) saves installation costs.

Operating Cost — This solution is among the most efficient overall for a grow room. Although each individual function of the unit (cooling, dehumidification) will not be as efficient as a dedicated system for those functions, the operating sequence ensures that there is not additional load placed on the equipment by disparate systems fighting each other in a space. Many unitary dehumidifiers are also equipped with efficiency boosting features such as variable-capacity compressors to ensure that as little energy as possible is used to treat the space.

Maintenance Cost — Unitary dehumidifiers are moderately complex, and thus moderately expensive to maintain. They are typically constructed from non-proprietary components that are readily available but will require a well-trained mechanical technician to perform repairs. Day-to-day maintenance is typically limited to cleaning the airpath and changing filters, although some manufacturers are still using obsolete technology, like fans with belt drives instead of direct drives, that reduce efficiency and increase maintenance costs.

EFFICIENCY

Cooling — These systems are moderately efficient at sensible cooling. As their coils are optimized for latent removal, there is typically a lower sensible heat ratio than ideal for a very efficient air conditioner. Newer technology like variable speed compressors and variable sensible heat ratio coils can boost air conditioning efficiency by two to three times.

Dehumidification — With dehumidification as their priority, these systems are an ideal solution for latent requirements.

Precision — Unitary systems are designed to provide tight space control, but in operation vary from adequate to excellent, depending on how appropriately sized they are and whether they include newer technologies. In order to guarantee success, ensure that you select a manufacturer who provides equipment incorporating the latest in unit control technologies. These systems are typically sized by the manufacturer, who is usually most qualified to understand the load calculations and their effect on equipment selection.

DESIGN

Complexity — These systems are relatively simple to design and install, because of their semi-standard nature and being limited to a single room of a building.

Scalability — Scalability is inherent in the design and is one of the biggest advantages of unitary dehumidifiers. Since they don't rely on building-wide infrastructure, individual grow rooms can be brought online without affecting the balance of the building, allowing for very easy scaling of operation.

Redundancy — Redundancy needs to be built into the overall system by either using multiple units in a space or by ensuring that the unitary system has internal redundancies, or both. Carefully examine proposed solutions to ensure that your risk tolerance is met.

PRODUCTION/SAFETY

Operational flexibility — Unitary systems are very flexible within a single space, allowing for a wide range of operating conditions both during lights on, lights off and end of grow setbacks. This flexibility allows a facility to change strains, growing conditions, and operating parameters on a per-room basis with ease.

Reliability — These systems apply technology that has been used for decades on a commercial scale, and are typically very reliable especially with modern components. Some manufacturers have product designs with built-in redundancy and typically multiple units will be used on a site thus eliminating single point of failure risks. A properly installed and maintained system should perform for 15–25 years without difficulty.

Plant Safety — Split unitary systems may have refrigerant charges that approach potentially hazardous levels for both human and/or plant health in the event of a catastrophic leak. Technologies exist in water-cooled designs to reduce the overall refrigerant charge to levels that greatly mitigate this risk. Facility design can help to isolate the grow room and its occupants from the refrigerant charge.

SUPPLEMENTAL DEHUMIDIFICATION

Supplemental Dehumidification — No supplemental dehumidification will be required with a properly sized and installed system.

SUMMARY

Unitary solutions are relatively new to the grow industry but are rapidly growing in popularity as they are an easily deployed, very agile solution. If properly conceived, they can allow a grower to maintain good control of their rooms while simultaneously balancing system cost, installation cost, and reliability.

A facility can begin with the minimum capacity it needs for start-up and then add more units in the future as required. They are usually cheaper to install than a central chilled water system and offer several reliability and efficiency benefits as well.

The real business advantage to this approach is that it opens up the grower's cash flow by spreading out their costs over time, rather than a large, immediate cost to construct the entire facility and chiller for day one. By going unitary, capital costs scale on a linear basis.

MISTAKES THAT CAN JEOPARDIZE YOUR PROJECT

CHAPTER 09

We've spent the last few chapters in this book discussing the many aspects that go into designing for a highly successful indoor growing environment.

The fundamentals of equipment procurement and building design have been covered. We've gone over practical information on getting the best HVAC equipment, growing conditions, and what you need to know about lighting. All this information will help provide any grower or engineer with the knowledge they need to oversee and execute new construction or renovation for a grow room.

Unlike many other subjects in the construction field, there is not much widely known information about grow room design and control practices. Many growers know a lot about plant science but have not typically been exposed to well-researched information on the indoor environment. There also is not much learned experience on topics such as getting the best value out of equipment and selecting the right manufacturer supplier. Knowledge about these issues can be very inconsistent.

As a result, there are some common mistakes that can be made by almost anyone and hold the potential to limit your grow room project's success. The consequences of these mistakes vary, but in all cases, they could possibly damage your long-term viability by reducing your business effectiveness, increasing your operating expenses, reducing your crop output and quality, or various other problems.

Let's review some of the most serious errors and how you can avoid them in your project.

NOT UNDERSTANDING AND ARTICULATING YOUR DESIRES

Many problems that can happen in a project trickle down from the fact that people involved in the project are not entirely clear on what kind of results the grower is seeking.

It's very important that you nail down early in the project exactly what it is you're looking for, why you're looking for that, and to communicate it clearly.

> Growers can avoid many issues with construction or retrofit projects simply by communicating their needs with detail and clarity.

Grower expectations can vary quite a bit depending on the type of facility and intended final use of the product. What is needed for fine bud may not be the same as what is required for oil extracts. As a result, key design factors such as the type and intensity of lighting and temperatures/humidity levels for each room must be agreed on by all involved parties. These operating conditions form the basis for all other aspects of the design as well as the capital, operating, and maintenance costs of equipment required to maintain desired conditions.

Considering different product purposes and grower expectations, clearly there is no "one size fits all" formula for the "perfect" or even "standard" grow facility. Each project should be approached with a blank slate and designed with specific goals in mind.

Ensure that you have every aspect of the space conditions and related factors agreed on before you move into the design phase, in what's called a "design intent" document, created by the project engineer. This is the only way to ensure that the project will meet grower expectations and also stay within the allocated budget.

The first and single most important step in grow room design is for all parties to meet during the preliminary stages. By involving everyone from the start, you can clarify expectations for the project at the initial stage. This vital step ensures that everyone is on the same page and lays the foundation to keep the project on track. An initial meeting is both time and cost effective, plus it goes a long way to establishing a good working relationship with everybody involved in the project.

Do not use "expected" operating conditions from a generic table. Everyone should take the time to review the requirements of this specific grow room. While we have listed the most commonly used space conditions for different types of rooms in Chapter 4: Navigating the Building Design Process, it's important to be aware that some facilities operate with temperatures and humidity requirements outside of what we would generally consider as standard. It is essential to recognize that different grow rooms may call for different conditions either due to their strain, plant species, or intended purpose.

Grow rooms can have very different needs depending on their use and the kind of crop that will occupy the space. Therefore, relying on a table of "typical" conditions is not a best practice.

When expectations have been expressed and are understood by everyone involved in the design process, it's time to figure out which solutions can satisfy the requirements.

Of course, the grower's capital and equipment installation budgets must be sufficient to get quality equipment that will serve their needs.

Value engineering should be avoided: this is where chosen HVAC equipment is pared down to the brass tacks in terms of function and options, in order to meet budget. While it's important for the grower and design team to collaborate on selecting the best equipment solution, there should be careful consideration about removing useful and money-saving features to bring down first-cost.

Choosing packaged, unitary equipment can be cheaper to install and often cheaper to maintain, as well. The designer should be mindful of the difference in capital expenditure and installation budget. While some equipment can be more expensive to buy, you might save enough on installation and ongoing operation and maintenance to make it a worthwhile investment.

Similarly, operating budget needs to be considered in the planning stage. Every cost, from energy to water, materials to maintenance, should be factored in.

If for some reason the projected operating costs are higher than the available budget, you might have to go back to the drawing board and determine what you can adjust to bring costs back down. Remember that energy costs will be volatile over time and inflation will also have its impact. So, to play it safe, it's advisable to make sure that the operating costs fall well within the budget and do not reach the upper end of what's affordable. This is also why it's very important to strive for energy-efficient equipment as it provides more predictability in the long term.

The design engineer can combine information about the operating conditions with data about the costs of energy and maintenance to attempt to project how much it will cost to operate the grow room.

Remember that even on projects where it might be tempting to predict low operating costs in order to soothe budget concerns, it is in nobody's interest to do so. When it comes to budgeting for maintenance, remember that regular, high-quality upkeep of the equipment can mean the difference between getting a 5-year or a 20-year lifespan out of the equipment. Maintenance can also significantly affect equipment efficiency and performance which, in turn, affect your yield and operating income.

Once the operating conditions are agreed on by all involved parties, including and especially the grower, make sure to create a document recording the exact conditions to serve as a reminder of what was agreed.

If expectations are not firmly decided on and communicated, the grower could end up with the wrong solutions for their needs.

MISGUIDED VALUE ENGINEERING

Value engineering is a technique used in project management that seeks to decrease the purchase price of equipment. Ideally, it would result in a product that costs less but delivers the same performance as a more expensive option.

It's often used in a budget crunch to bring down the price of HVAC equipment in grow rooms through the elimination of several key functions that contribute to a good environment. The thinking is that, while these features are important, they are not technically required for the unit to operate. But this represents a profound misunderstanding of how these features work and the value of having them in place.

There is also a misunderstanding of the difference between first-cost and total cost of ownership. Often, in the bid and procurement process, there is a motivation to obtain equipment at the lowest possible first-cost. However, this analysis neglects the overall investment of buying equipment which, if done correctly, will pay dividends for many years in reduced costs for operating and maintaining the unit.

Selecting equipment for a grow room is an investment in the facility. Spending more allows you to get better equipment that offers more high-performance features that improve efficiency and longevity. Just like any other product, there are HVAC manufacturers that offer cheaper, but inferior, products. Avoiding this low-quality equipment is important if you're aiming for a high-performing facility.

While value engineering is a legitimate technique to use when there is a limited capital budget in place, everybody involved in the project should understand the dangers of seeking only the lowest bid.

The optimal balance of capital-cost, installation costs, and maintenance and operating costs will deliver outstanding return-on-investment for the grower.

First-cost is, simply, the initial cost to buy the equipment. It considers factors like whether there is any add-on features to the HVAC (like economizer cooling or heat recovery) and can vary depending on the brand and quality of equipment. Some manufacturers use cheaper components that result in equipment that offers less performance and durability. First-cost can also be called capital cost and that is usually how it's expressed in a budget line. It should not be confused with installation cost, which usually is separately expressed on a capital budget.

Installation carries its own costs that need to be carefully considered in the total purchase price.

Total cost of ownership is everything that happens after first-cost, such as the cost of energy to run the unit, the effort required the maintain it, whether the grower will need expensive repairs, and how soon the unit will need replacement. Total cost of ownership can easily, over time, eclipse the first-cost of some equipment. Therefore, both of these costs must be estimated and considered before making any buying decisions. Spending more on the front-end (CAPEX) can avoid greater costs on the back-end (OPEX).

There is some degree of bias in the design and construction industry to favor, in these types of projects, the lowest first-cost with little or no consideration toward the total cost of ownership. That's because the people involved in procurement are typically not involved in the facility on an ongoing basis after the project is completed. In most cases, the contractor must support the unit for only one year after installation.

The grower should get involved in the procurement of their equipment because they will be saddled with the long-term costs associated with whatever is purchased. They need to understand what the cost breakdown is for all the equipment that's being considered in order to decide what works best for their business objectives. The grower should ask many questions and make sure they are being told the reasons for certain equipment recommendations and existing alternatives.

There are some features for HVAC that are considered "optional" add-ons. These may include economizer cooling and heat recovery. These features may be eliminated to pare down the cost of the equipment. But does it really result in the same performance? And is eliminating some of these features a smart investment?

Let's take, for example, heat recovery. This should be included on any unitary HVAC installed in a grow room because it can use compressor hot gas to pre-heat cold air coming off the dehumidifier coil before it goes back into the space, therefore reducing the need for additional heat sources. If the feature is not included in the equipment, the grower needs to spend more running supplementary heaters that represent an ongoing cost. How much did you really save?

The engineer and grower should consider the longer-term benefits and savings of a feature like this before deciding to eliminate it. It's a good idea for the engineer to work with the manufacturer on calculating the ROI before arriving at a decision. Many energy-saving features offer rapid payback.

Equivalencies are another thing to watch out for. Sometimes in value engineering, there is an effort to substitute cheaper equipment that is purported to do the same thing or deliver the same performance. This is not always the case and the grower and engineer should be cautious about choosing alternatives.

Equipment specifications are often quite loose. Although they are drawn out of a basis of design that was generated with a specific product from a specific brand in mind, specifications are usually not as explicit as their name would suggest. They generally describe the minimum requirements of equipment but don't often spell out key competitive features. In effect, this means almost any unit from any brand could "meet" the specifications.

An equivalence is when proposed equipment is significantly different from the basis of design, but technically meets the specifications. Usually, the performance is inferior to what formed the basis of design. This could be chosen as part of value engineering or may be chosen independently by the contractor; they are often hired at a fixed price and may be motivated to procure the lowest-cost equipment in order to maximize their profit. Sometimes they look for equipment that does not follow all the specifications in order to reduce their cost to provide equipment.

For example, the basis of design may have been a cutting-edge unit with fully-coated coils, heat rejection to a dry cooler with economizer cooling mode. But the selected equipment could easily have only fin-coated coils, or even use split-DX. It is not uncommon for contractors to select equipment that ignores some of the specifications.

If the engineer does not inspect the selected equipment to ensure it follows specifications, or the grower does not take an active role in the process, then these false equivalencies are par for the course.

The bottom line here is that the grower should take an interest in how their equipment is selected to ensure it serves their needs, and not somebody else's.

Another important issue to consider that is easily forgotten is how much maintenance the selected equipment will require.

Every piece of equipment needs some attention periodically. For HVAC, that is especially true if there is to be any expectation of trouble-free operation over many years.

But cheaper equipment can require closer attention than those of a higher grade.

Take, for example, dry coolers. They offer many benefits over the traditional split-DX solution involving an outdoor air-cooled condenser. They also offer significantly reduced annual maintenance requirements.

For one, the right dry cooler can have virtually self-cleaning condensing coils. Imagine the ease of use for the grower that comes with not having to frequently clean the outdoor unit!

Dry coolers, unlike OACCs, simply use water and a little bit of glycol as their cooling medium, which means they don't have to be opened twice a year to balance the charge. With OACCs, the refrigerant charge must be matched to winter and summer conditions. This requires expensive skilled technicians and some equipment downtime.

Contrast this twice-annual maintenance requirement with a typical glycol loop maintenance schedule of a full drain and fill approximately every three years with water and inexpensive glycol.

When coupled with the other benefits of dry coolers as described in Chapter 8: HVAC System Types, the grower stands to gain plenty by going with this type of equipment even if the initial investment is higher than for an OACC.

By choosing higher-quality components that are more efficient and require less annual maintenance, facilities can realize greater profit over time.

DON'T TAKE A PIECEMEAL/BAND-AID APPROACH

Creating a grow facility needs to be a holistic process that considers all the systems as contributing to one environment.

The grower needs to have a plan for how they're going to tackle every aspect in the near and long term.

Most growers build their facilities in multiple stages, which is a smart way to go, but there needs to be some detailed central planning behind it. Know how you're going to scale that first phase after it's built.

It's also important that everything be ready when it's time to hit the "on" switch, figuratively speaking. If you try to get started, for example, with your HVAC equipment but the building management software is not yet operational, there could be serious problems that occur as a result of launching a half-baked system.

The same goes for relying on cheap band-aid solutions for problems entirely created by short-sighted decisions in the design process. An example of this are extra fans many growers have added to their rooms to increase air churn. Why do they do this? Because the HVAC specifications are insufficient to provide the turnover a grow facility needs. While they do improve the churn, it comes at a cost of adding more heat into the space, something often not accounted for in the cooling load calculations. These fans are also difficult to clean effectively, meaning they create a contamination risk. These are all problems that could have been avoided by making the right decisions earlier in the process.

> While regular maintenance for all equipment is important, investing in the kind of equipment that will require less attention over the course of a year is a great way to reduce downtime and costs. The same is true for minimizing the pieces of equipment in a facility.

DON'T PICK VENDORS. PICK PARTNERS.

Picking someone who is looking to be a vendor to you, and not a partner, is a potential mistake for your business.

A partner in this sense means someone you work with who genuinely has your company's best interests in mind. (We don't mean "partner" here in terms of a formal, legal business partnership.)

The market is full of vendors and consultants who all say they have just what every grower needs. With so many choices, it makes no sense for a grower to select someone who is only interested in making the sale. Instead, you should choose someone who is invested in working with you for the long haul to ensure your total success.

A partner is more like a friend, whereas a vendor is not. Partners understand your business, including all aspects, not just the particular area they deal with. Partners want to help solve your problems. They should be willing to provide advice based on their experience, even if it means there may be no sale in the end. Partners are willing to make what they sell work for you, and keep it working for the long term.

The reason you should be looking for partners, and not vendors, is because the former will be devoted to your ongoing success long after the sale, whereas the latter will be less engaged. In this industry, trust is everything, so you need to be able to trust your suppliers as well. Pick suppliers who will be partners.

When you have found one you trust, put that trust where it matters and collaborate with them on whatever solution they are providing. As noted elsewhere in this book, there is certain key information you need to provide to an HVAC partner to allow them to investigate the right equipment for your needs. Because of the proprietary nature of this business, most growers would only feel comfortable about discussing some of these details with someone they trust — a partner, not just any vendor.

Listen to your partner's recommendations, particularly when it comes to installing their equipment and interfacing it with your grow rooms. Not all solutions are the same, and what may have worked in a previous phase or with previous equipment may not work the same way with new gear. Just as how the master grower knows about their plants, manufacturers know about their equipment, and it takes two to tango. This work requires a high level of trust and confidence in each other, which is why it's so important you find a manufacturer you can consider a partner.

CONCLUSION

The grower needs to have a clear understanding of their expectations before starting the design or retrofit of a facility, and these expectations must be clearly communicated to everyone involved in the project from the engineer and contractor to equipment vendors.

Grow facilities are expensive. Don't jeopardize your long-term success to save 10% on your building; a year later, that 10% will be inconsequential compared to the headaches and lost revenue caused by short-sighted decision-making. So, before value engineering away valuable money-saving features in HVAC equipment, consider the long-term payback of having them.

Get design right the first time; band-aid solutions will not help you and will weigh you down with baggage like inefficiencies and added maintenance tasks. By all means, build in phases. But there ought to be longer-term planning to support future scaling-up.

Do not end up surrounded by vendors who will sell you whatever makes them money and then seldom be seen again. In this industry, with so many manufacturers and consultants looking to earn your business, it makes no sense to settle for that. Instead you should seek to partner with companies and people you trust who will work with you to ensure your total success, long after any sale.

IMPORTANT INSTALLATION AND START-UP TIPS

CHAPTER 10

Designing the right HVAC system for a grow room and making sure the grower is informed about all of the available options are both critical steps. You must also ensure that good quality equipment is purchased for the facility.

With these steps completed, it is now time to install the equipment and set the stage for a long and trouble-free service life.

However, there are several additional design and installation issues to keep in mind to ensure the unit can be properly installed, as well as adequately serviced and maintained.

Before beginning installation, the contractor should be familiar with the job site and relevant documentation from the manufacturer such as drawings and submittals.

REQUIRED ACCESS SPACE

A serious and recurring problem in any HVAC application is that the facility does not allocate sufficient space to access and service the HVAC unit. In some places, the HVAC system is tucked away tightly in a corner or even hidden in the ceiling.

Of course, it's understandable that one would want to maximize the space for growing as commercial space comes at a premium, but this should never come at the expense of the equipment or the people hired to maintain and service it.

When the equipment is not easily accessible, it's simply not going to be properly maintained. This lack of maintenance will inevitably result in failure and cost the grower an enormous amount in repair and replacement bills, additional expenses due to compromised performance and, in the worst case scenario, the financial impact of a decline in business.

> It's vital that the HVAC unit is easily accessible so that it can be properly maintained and serviced. All technicians and maintenance personnel should be instructed that, if they feel that accessing a piece of equipment will put them at risk, they shouldn't touch it at all. Nothing is worth putting their personal safety at risk.

Be sure to follow the manufacturer's requirements to determine which sides of the unit need access space and how much space is needed. Carefully review the submittal for specific details.

Outdoor condensers or coolers also require a fair amount of clear space around them to properly function. Follow manufacturer guidelines, which are generally 36 inches all around and at least 96 inches above the fan.

In some locations, regulations may require the equipment to be fully washdown-capable in between grows. This is required in Canada, for example, so be sure to check the local regulations and ensure you provide enough space in the installation to get cleaning equipment in and spray the unit's interior.

Some manufacturers offer fully-coated coils and airpath to enable simple washing of the interior. Fully-coated coils allow for the use of potentially corrosive air treatment practices in the grow room. Further, a fully-coated coil and drain pan may allow for the recycling of condensate for watering plants without concerns for metal oxide contamination.

RECEIVING THE UNIT

Any good unit manufacturer will inspect and fully test their products before shipping from the factory, but damage does sometimes happen during transit. It's incumbent on the installer/receiver to carefully inspect the equipment upon arrival to ensure it is in good order and there was no damage during shipping, and no parts are missing. Whoever is receiving the unit should conduct a thorough visual and hands-on check for damage before signing the receiving papers.

Here's a checklist to run through:

- Visually inspect exterior of the equipment for damage (scratches, dents, missing elements, etc.)
- Verify the proper operation of latches and hinges on all access doors.
- Inspect all coils for damage to the fin surface coating, headers, or coil connections.
- Manually rotate the fan wheel to ensure free movement of the shaft, bearings, and drive.

- Inspect the fan housings for any foreign objects.
- Inspect and test all piping for possible shipping damage.
- Check the tightness of bolts on the fan structure and coils.
- Inspect fan isolator shipping brackets.

Typically, shipping units is freight-on-board (FOB), which means that the equipment belongs to the customer when it leaves the factory.

If you note any shipping damage, you must detail it on the freight bill and bill of lading. Take clear photographs of the damaged areas and obtain a claim form from the carrier to fill out and return. All claims must be reported as soon as possible to the carrier. You may need to coordinate an inspection by the carrier as well to verify. Delivery cannot be refused on the basis of shipping damage.

As that is being done, also contact the manufacturer and have the unit serial number ready. The serial number can be found on the equipment's main label or bill of lading.

It's the receiver's responsibility to provide evidence that damage happened before it was delivered, so make sure to document the damage thoroughly. Don't try fixing it yourself without consulting the manufacturer.

STORAGE

Many times, units are not installed and started-up right away because the facility remains under construction.

Be sure to keep indoor units in a protected location if they are going to be stored for some time before being installed in their final location. Long term storage in a controlled indoor environment is strongly recommended. Keep in mind, most manufacturer warranties expire after a certain number of months after the unit is shipped, even if it isn't started-up. For outdoor units, check with the manufacturer for recommendations on long term storage prior to installation.

> Ideally, units go directly from the manufacturer to the customer site rather than a third-party storage facility or rigging yard to minimize the risk of damage due to handling and transport.

LIFTING AND RIGGING

Lifting and rigging must be done by trained professionals in accordance with proper lifting techniques and safety procedures. Proper lifting machinery and tools and safety equipment/personal protective equipment (PPE) must be used. Improper lifting may cause equipment damage, serious injury, or death. This is a high-risk task and should be conducted in accordance with a written plan.

Use spreader bars for lifting to prevent equipment damage. The cables may not necessarily be of the same length. Adjust as necessary for an even lift. Determine the approximate center of gravity before lifting. You can get the total weight and weight distribution from the submittal documentation. Lift points will be illustrated.

Important safety tips for lifting:

- Each of the lifting cables (chains or slings) must be able to support the entire weight of the equipment.
- Do not lift in windy conditions.
- Never lift with personnel directly below.
- Perform a test lift of the equipment about 20–30 inches above the ground to verify the lifting equipment is working properly and you have an even lift.
- To avoid damage, do not attach intake or exhaust hoods prior to lifting.

GENERAL PLACEMENT

The specific placement of the equipment and nature of its installation may vary by job. The contractor should refer to the submittal for more details.

However, some general information should be kept in mind. Units should always be installed on a firm, level surface with vibration absorption features. Manufacturers will state what their required access room is and on which sides it is necessary.

INSTALLING INDOORS

If the unit is to be installed in a mechanical room:

- Other materials stored in the mechanical room cannot block required access space.
- The mechanical room must have an operational floor drain.
- Do not attempt an indoor installation of condensers or coolers that are intended for outdoor use.

A ceiling-mount of the unit is sometimes possible. Refer to submittal for weight distribution details to properly select and position supports. Unit must be supported from the base while mounting. Always remember, anything you hang in the space has the potential to block airflow paths. Good airflow is the key to successful indoor growing.

OUTDOOR INSTALLATION

In the grow room application, indoor installations are generally preferred as they are more contained and can thus help avoid the risk of contamination. If an outdoor installation is necessary, then only use units intended for outdoor use. They are designed for the harsh conditions found outside year-round. Ensure that the manufacturer provides a unit that can be totally sealed from the outside, with sturdy, insulated cabinet construction.

The unit must be designed to work in cold temperatures if it will be installed outside in a northern locale. If the unit is not insulated, for example, condensation could form inside the unit, promoting corrosion as well as the risk of contamination.

If the unit is installed on a roof curb, it must use curb gasket material to create a moisture and weather seal between the unit and a roof curb. Before placing onto a roof curb, consider accessibility underneath the unit for various mechanical and electrical systems connections (power, drain, other piping, etc.) It is not recommended to use space within a roof curb as a supply or return duct.

Outdoor installations should consider the direction of prevailing winds. They may negatively affect equipment operation (cross-flow of exhausted and fresh air and/or flue gases, elements seeping into outdoor air opening, etc.)

OUTDOOR AIR-COOLED CONDENSER OR DRY COOLER INSTALLATION

These pieces of equipment reject unneeded heat from the space to the outdoors and provide air-conditioning capability. One of the aspects of grow room design that is often overlooked is that the hot air off these items needs to be able to flow away, which always makes it imperative that there's open space around outdoor heat rejection devices.

Avoid installing outdoor condensers or coolers in a pit where they're surrounded by a wall on all sides. This impedes their access to fresh air, which is needed for the unit to function properly. If such an installation can't be avoided, then the minimum clearance (36 inches around and a minimum of 96 inches above the fan) should be doubled and the pit cannot be taller than the equipment.

Moreover, the air that is discharged must not be allowed to recirculate. Without proper airflow, the system will eventually trip on high pressure.

The easiest way to ensure proper airflow is to adhere to the following guidelines at installation:

- Ensure an appropriate maximum ambient air temperature has been specified.
- Ensure the unit has proper airflow and follows manufacturer's guidelines for free space around all units.
- Do not install near other sources of hot air. For example, do not place an air-cooled condenser above another as the hot air from the lower one will rise and be sucked in by the higher one.
- To avoid potential seasonal system charge problems with outdoor condensers, ensure the installed line lengths are never longer than indicated on the plans and specifications. Generally, 50 feet is the working maximum for split-DX systems.
- If the condenser is installed above the unit, ensure the hot gas line has proper oil traps.
- Contact manufacturer if the condenser is installed more than eight feet below the unit.
- Specify that OACC lines be nitrogen-purged while being brazed to help avoid scaling within the pipe.

Note that all of these challenging refrigeration requirements disappear if you opt for a water-cooled system.

Water-cooled systems have another advantage with grow rooms: they are more suited to providing cooling even during the winter.

> Always ensure sufficient breathing room for the outdoor heat rejector. Without a good airflow, the system will trip on high pressure!

CONTROL WIRING TO THE INTERNET

Putting your unit system online (if the manufacturer offers web-based monitoring) is a critical aspect of ensuring peak performance at all times. Some IT work, which isn't the first thing you'd expect in grow room design, is probably responsible for this step often slipping through the cracks. Unfortunately, when this happens and the unit cannot be connected online, the grow room operator misses out on all of the benefits of an online microprocessor, including:

- Collection of data 24/7 for the lifetime of the system.
- Quick service response time.
- No need for a technician to make a site visit in many cases.
- Analyzing data to optimize performance and prevent incidents.

All that is needed is to ensure an ethernet connection is available where the unit is to be installed. If that is impractical, then a strong dedicated Wi-Fi network could be used instead. It may also be possible to connect the unit via cell network, although data charges may add up over time.

Plan to get the unit connected to the internet during the design phase. Make sure there's either an ethernet cable called out in the design or that there's a strong Wi-Fi signal at the location where the unit will be installed.

START-UP AND COMMISSIONING

Start-up and commissioning are typically performed by the installing contractor. It's recommended that a factory or factory-trained HVAC technician also be on-site to supervise these processes and to ensure a trouble-free start to service life. They'll also be able to provide expert training to facility staff on the basic care and maintenance of the unit.

The unit will ship with a start-up packet containing step-by-step guidance on what the contractor must do to start-up the unit.

Remember, the equipment contains refrigerant under high pressure, moving mechanical components, and high voltage powered components: exercise caution while performing start-up or other work!

Before scheduling a visit from the manufacturer, make sure all systems are ready and tested, and that the OACC or water-cooled heat rejection device has been installed and charged. Power to the unit must be active for at least 24 hours prior to start-up, to power-up the compressor's crankcase heater.

The unit is usually started-up in an empty grow room to evaluate its performance and confirm every aspect of its operation. The final performance review is called "commissioning" and can only be completed once the grow room is operating at design conditions.

In order to properly commission equipment, it must be operating under the same load and conditions it will see during regular service. This is typically difficult to achieve prior to plants installed in the grow space. Consult with your manufacturer for advice on creating an artificial test environment.

The grower needs to be alerted that it would be unwise to attempt a grow before the grow automation system is online. Even if the HVAC is running fine, it is critical that all of the systems be tied together before any cultivation can begin.

CONCLUSION

If you keep these points in mind, the payoff is that you'll get the installation right from the start. Nobody wants operations to start off poorly because installation was done incorrectly.

Always ensure sufficient access space is provided so the unit can be serviced. Failure to do so will likely mean the unit is not given the maintenance it needs, and that will affect equipment life.

Proper installation relies on there being a way to get the unit where it needs to be. Whether this is on a roof or in a mechanical room, be sure to install it on a solid and level surface and follow all manufacturer instructions for proper installation. The submittal is a helpful resource to refer to and has useful information such as the weight of the unit and its weight distribution, which will help in the lifting and rigging.

Ensuring an ethernet cable is available at the installation location will allow the unit to be connected to manufacturer provided internet monitoring. The benefit of these services should not be overlooked as they help greatly in ensuring the unit is running efficiently and fixed quickly if anything goes wrong.

CARE AND MAINTENANCE OF PRECISION HVAC

CHAPTER 11

If properly taken care of, a good-quality grow room HVAC system can last a very long time.

While the normal service life for a unitary dehumidifier is around 10 years, it is entirely possible for a machine to remain in great shape entering its 20s. Growers can benefit greatly from following a regular maintenance routine to keep their unit(s) in tip-top shape, therefore delivering value for many years, well beyond its typical expected lifespan. If you want to keep your equipment for a long time for the lowest possible cost in operation and maintenance, it's important to get a premium product that will deliver the reliability you need.

It may seem obvious that such a high-performance piece of equipment needs a little tender, loving care to keep it running properly. But it's easy to forget. In some facilities, maintenance of the HVAC unit is forgotten about or rarely done. This could be for a variety of reasons; for example, the unit is in a difficult-to-access space, or there is a lack of time, a lack of knowledge, or lack of a service contract.

But basic maintenance for these units is quite simple and should never be viewed as a "nice to have." If a grower has any expectation for a long and trouble-free life out of their HVAC equipment, it's an absolute must to have regular and scheduled maintenance of the equipment. Putting in the minimal resources required to perform some key tasks can pay off by avoiding expensive repairs or even replacement sooner than would otherwise be necessary. Preventative maintenance is always the better investment, rather than major repairs after something breaks.

Fortunately, many of the most important maintenance tasks do not need special technical knowledge to perform. Generally, any facility maintenance staff who are technically inclined should be able to perform these tasks. That means you can easily keep your equipment in great shape without constantly needing to call in a specialized service company for repairs that could have been avoided. In addition to regular basic maintenance and inspection, the equipment should be inspected by a highly qualified service technician at least annually.

SAFETY FIRST

Only qualified and properly trained personnel should attempt to perform maintenance tasks.

It's recommended that facility staff receive training from the manufacturer or a factory-authorized service company when the unit is installed so they can be brought up to speed on the same maintenance tasks outlined in this chapter. The pointers in this chapter are meant as a general guide for performing certain maintenance tasks.

Safety should always be the priority and personnel should not perform any task that they feel unsafe or uncomfortable doing.

We take no responsibility for any personal injury or equipment damage caused by improper practice of maintenance on equipment. The information in this chapter is to be used as a guideline, but we recommend checking with your manufacturer for information on performing all routine maintenance tasks.

- Before performing any maintenance, disconnect all electrical power, including remote disconnect, and discharge all energy storing devices (VFDs, etc.) before servicing. Follow proper lockout and tagout procedures to ensure that power cannot be accidentally restored. Do not simply turn the device "off" at the control panel. Failure to disconnect the unit from power and to follow provided safety warnings and labels could result in serious injury or death.
- Be aware of potential hazards. The equipment contains moving mechanical parts, components with refrigerant under high pressure, and surfaces with extremely high or low temperatures. Before entering the HVAC unit and/or performing any equipment maintenance work, make sure that all moving parts are stopped, and it is safe to perform required tasks.
- Certain tasks outside the scope of this chapter may require specialized personnel to accomplish. For example, when it is necessary to work with live

electrical components, have a licensed electrician or other qualified professional perform the task.

- Some maintenance tasks may involve the usage of power tools, chemicals, etc. Refer to such tools and materials data (manuals, MSDS, etc.) Personnel performing such maintenance tasks should be:
    - properly trained to handle such tools and materials safely; and
    - equipped with proper personal protective equipment.

SAMPLE MAINTENANCE SCHEDULE

Every facility should have a maintenance schedule where key tasks are assigned a date on which they will be performed.

This will ensure these tasks are not forgotten, which is a common reason why facilities fall behind on their maintenance routine. You should perform these tasks **between every grow cycle** or as **otherwise required by your local jurisdiction**. Given the highly precise nature of cannabis growing, especially in enclosed facilities without sunlight, it is critical to ensure that your HVAC unit remains in excellent working condition and is as clean as possible. When a set of crop finishes their stay in a specific room and is moved into another for the next stage of their growth, the HVAC should be cleaned just as thoroughly as the rest of the room.

The following is a list of some key preventative maintenance tasks.

On a weekly basis

- Observe the equipment for any changes in operation. For example, unusual noises, leaks, etc.

After each grow cycle

- Replace air filters.
- Verify that all set-points are correctly programmed as per the unit design and room purpose.
- Inspect and clean the drain pan(s).
- Inspect all airstream coils for dirt, cobweb build-up, etc.; clean as needed.
- Check that the P-trap is primed (filled with water). It is good practice to pour some water into the drain pan to ensure that the P-trap is primed and operational. If it's not primed, the low-pressure interior of the unit will suck air up through the drain, making it impossible for water to flow away and therefore resulting in it overflowing.
- Check the outdoor air louvers and dampers for accumulation of dirt, debris and dust, and clean as required.
- Clean the fan wheel(s).
- Wash down the entire interior of the cabinet with warm water and soap. When buying your equipment, consider whether this task will be possible. Some regulations may require that equipment be fully washdown capable. If the unit is installed indoors, use an operational floor drain in the mechanical room.

Semi-Annually

- Tighten electrical connections, if required.
- Check and tighten, if required, hose clamps and sensor mounts.

- Inspect the equipment's cabinet for corrosion. If any damage is found, clean and repaint the affected surface with a rust-resistant coating.
- Inspect and clean outdoor condenser/cooler coils.

Annually

- Check damper operation (ensure linkage/actuator is not loose, verify dampers open/close properly, etc.)
- Inspect electrical components, wiring and insulation.
- Rotate the fan wheel(s) and check for obstructions and rubbing.
- Check gasket condition on all doors to ensure an airtight seal.
- Check bolts on compressors, motor mounts, HVAC unit bases and coils, and tighten if required.
- Verify that the airflow around the remote condenser or dry cooler is unobstructed.

KEY POINTS

Here are some important maintenance considerations relevant to all HVAC units and their auxiliary systems:

- No chemicals (for example, pesticides) should be stored in the same room where the HVAC unit is installed. Chemical fumes can cause premature deterioration of the equipment and contamination of the grow room. Chemicals should instead be kept in a separate and well-ventilated room.
- Required access space must be given in the installation. Manufacturer guidelines for minimum clearances are designed to allow for maintenance access in both indoor and outdoor settings.

One issue to keep in mind, beyond routine maintenance, is that not all HVAC technicians are qualified to diagnose or fix advanced technology machines. Unitary dehumidifiers are notably different than standard air conditioners and that limits the pool of qualified personnel if major maintenance work is required. Choosing an equipment vendor who can support their product after the sale is essential.

KEEPING AN EYE ON THINGS

Some very simple, yet crucial, advice is: keep track of how the unit is operating.

Anybody who works near the unit should take note if they're hearing any different noises. Different noises or other issues are not normal and could be a sign that something is wrong.

Taking the opportunity to conduct a quick inspection could save you from major repairs or component replacements shortly down the road.

Nothing is more helpful to keeping tabs on your HVAC unit than connecting it to web monitoring, if the feature is available. All that is typically required is a dedicated ethernet cable to plug into the web monitor interface. Connections via Wi-Fi or cellular network are also possible although not recommended due to their decreased reliability.

Once online, the unit is constantly uploading operational data to the factory servers in real time, 24/7.

This technology makes life a breeze for operators and service technicians alike. By having a full history of the unit's operation stored in the cloud, diagnostics are streamlined. Service personnel can log in on their computer, smartphone, or tablet to see this history along with all historical alarms that have been raised with the unit. They can also adjust dozens of operating parameters right from their devices. In many cases, minor issues or inefficiencies with the HVAC unit can be resolved like this, even by off-site personnel.

If ever an alarm is raised, the system can be set up to alert service contractors or other key people via email instantly. Because it's possible to log into the unit from anywhere, the factory can provide live support remotely to aid in troubleshooting. As a result, equipment downtime is significantly reduced and expensive repairs or in-person visits can often be avoided.

Compare this system to an unconnected unit that isn't uploading a full history of its operation to web servers and instantly alerting operators of alarms. In this situation, technicians may have to pay an on-site visit to check out the unit and troubleshoot. Because the unit can't alert the operator immediately of any alarms raised, some problems may go unresolved until the equipment fails.

AIR FILTERS

Dehumidifiers are equipped with air filters, often in multiple sets, that remove dust and other particulates from the air. They are found on the return air intake and are critical to ensuring good air quality in the space and for preventing mold spores circulating in the moist air, as well as for protecting the delicate coils.

Dehumidifier coils are typically several inches deep, which makes them hard to clean thoroughly if any dust gets into them. Additionally, the items caught by the filters from one crop could contaminate the next crop that enters the space. Therefore, the air filters must be changed consistently after each grow.

The good news is that filters are inexpensive and well worth the price of regular replacement, compared to what it will cost the owner through inefficiencies caused by dirty coils and the possibility of contaminating or losing a crop. Refer to the stickers on your equipment or submittal documents for the type of filter equipped (or the filters themselves). It's best for them to be MERV-13.

Higher-rated filters may not provide a real added benefit in reducing airborne particulates and will cost more in both fan energy costs (due to high pressure drop) and filter replacement costs.

Filter replacements can be purchased at any number of stores; just make sure they are the same rating for your dehumidifier and in the correct dimensions.

Do not change your filter type with a higher rating than the unit was designed for. Some manufacturers may have cost-effective filter replacement programs available.

AIRSIDE COILS

These critical components include the evaporator coil, re-heat coil, and coils inside the outdoor condensers/coolers.

The coils that come into contact with the process airstream should be checked and cleaned after every grow. Coils for the outdoor condenser/cooler should be checked approximately every six months.

Before beginning, tidy up the area around the coils and dehumidifier to make sure foreign objects won't get into the coils while the unit is opened for cleaning.

To clean, first remove any dust and other foreign objects from the surface of the coils. Ideally, do this by spraying water on the side of the coils opposite where air enters. If this backwashing is not possible, then use a vacuum cleaner or a soft-bristle brush. Be very gentle with the brush and apply motion in the direction of the fins. The fins can be bent and should be corrected if that happens.

Do not proceed with the rest of the cleaning procedure until surface fibers and dirt are removed. Otherwise, they could be driven deeper into the coil and make it harder to clean.

After you are satisfied that the surface is free of foreign objects, apply a solution to clean the coil. Often warm, soapy water will do the trick. The manufacturer of the coils may have their own set of recommended procedures, which can be obtained from the HVAC unit's manufacturer.

Apply cleaning solution to coils on the air-exit side using a pressure sprayer, generously soaking the coils for several minutes. Because the coils are very delicate, the pressure of the spray should be kept below 100 PSI. Use a medium-size nozzle that provides an even coating.

Coils may contain refrigerant under high pressure, so don't use a hot solution to clean them. A lukewarm or room-temperature solution is sufficient.

Airside coil fins are very thin to allow effective heat transfer. This also means they are very delicate, so handle with care! When cleaning, only apply motion in the direction of the fins.

It may be required to apply a second solution to remove mineral deposits from the coil. A solution such as CHLOR*RID® may be used for this. In most cases, use in a 100:1 mix ratio with potable water (2.56 ounce of solution to 1 gallon of water.)

Again, apply generously for several minutes with a pressurized sprayer that does not exceed 100 PSI. After an even application, rinse by spraying with potable water.

CHECK FOR CORROSION

Dehumidifiers are constantly exposed to a stream of humid air, so it is no surprise that their interior air corridors are at risk of corrosion.

Conduct a semi-annual visual inspection of the dehumidifier interior to check for corrosion in areas wherever the airstream may touch.

Some parts that commonly corrode:

- Airside coils, especially if they are not fully covered with an anticorrosion coating.
- Sheet metal, especially the edges. A good-quality dehumidifier should use treated metal to prevent corrosion.
- Galvanized or composite components like inlet cones for blowers and fan brackets.
- Piping.

If there is corrosion on any components, give them a thorough clean to remove contamination and cover with a rust-proof paint.

Insulation used on the inside of the dehumidifier should also be inspected for the possibility of mold growth.

CLEANING OF CABINET

Cabinets can get dirty over the course of weeks and months, especially the interior.

Make sure that dirt and dust doesn't build up by cleaning it after every grow stage. Wipe any tarnished parts of the cabinet with a wet rag with dish soap. Scrub the floor and walls of the cabinet and rinse with fresh water. A thorough clean will ensure the cabinet remains in good condition for many years by preventing corrosion from setting in. Before returning the unit to operation, ensure water has been wiped from the floor.

CHECK MOVING PARTS

On an annual basis, a hands-on inspection of key moving parts should be conducted. First, make sure the dehumidifier has been disconnected from the power source.

Manually rotate the fan wheels to ensure free movement. If the fan is belt-driven, check the belt and adjust or replace as needed. Clean the fan wheels with a rag dipped in soapy water. Check the dampers and make sure they operate unimpeded.

Examine the outdoor condenser or cooler and ensure its airflow is not obstructed. If it's installed in an area where fallen branches or debris such as leaves can collect, make sure to sweep regularly and clear them out. Obstructed airflow will cost the owner due to reduced efficiency.

ELECTRICAL PANEL

Another important annual preventative maintenance task is to have an electrician or otherwise qualified person inspect the unit's electrical and control panel(s). Over time, vibrations and temperature changes can loosen wires and they could break free. It does not happen often but is important to check.

CONCLUSION

This chapter outlined several simple yet key maintenance points every facility operator should follow on a regular basis. The average lifespan of a dehumidifier is around a decade. Reaching or exceeding that age is dependent on good and consistent maintenance. Not only will the owner save by having their unit last longer, they will also benefit by requiring fewer repairs or component replacements. A well-maintained dehumidifier also operates at peak efficiency, therefore using less energy to deliver the best possible performance.

FAQ

Here are some key frequently asked questions relevant to the contents of this book.

CROP AND HVAC

Q: What does HVAC have to do with plant yield, quality and consistency?

A: Yield, quality, and consistency are all dependent on stable and precise room conditions that enable the most efficient grow possible. HVAC equipment must be able to effectively control temperature and relative humidity levels in order to deliver the optimal vapor pressure differential within the space, critical for improving yield. RH levels also influence the risk of certain diseases or infections. Equipment that does not effectively control humidity levels can hobble the quality and consistency of the crop.

AIR DISTRIBUTION

Q: What is the most important factor to keep in mind regarding HVAC design for a grow room?

A: Get the air distribution right. That means getting air to the canopy and getting your plants fully covered by good airflow, approximately 0.5–1 m/s in velocity. Even if the rest of the design is perfect, if the air around the plants is stagnating, you will have serious problems. Focus on getting a good ductwork arrangement in the room to accomplish this so you don't have to rely on make-up fans in the space after the fact, because they are a contamination liability. Review Chapter 7 for more details on getting the best grow conditions.

Q: What is the recommended air change rate for grow rooms?

A: Hourly air changes of 40–50 is recommended.

Q: Are there any standards in place for grow room design?

A: No, there are no standards as of this writing. Further, the highly competitive nature of this industry means knowledge-sharing is not common.

DUCT MATERIAL

Q: What duct material is recommended?

A: Galvanized sheet metal, fabric duct, and aluminum are all suitable duct materials. Fabric ducts are becoming more common because they are affordable, can be ordered in any size, and are easily taken down and laundered in between grows for ease of cleanliness. Disposable ducts are also popular because they can be conveniently discarded and replaced after each grow.

RETURN AIR INTAKE LOCATION

Q: Where should I locate my return duct intake?

A: Your return duct intake must be in a position where it complements the supply duct air distribution pattern. If you have an overhead supply duct, then low returns are effective. If the facility is large, several return intakes are recommended.

There are two common ways to place supply air. In a small room, you can have supply air on one side and return on the other to push air in a linear direction through the space. In larger rooms, you may have to break it up into sections with multiple supply and returns. In that case, consider putting ducting in with the growing tiers. This is especially useful if you have multi-level tiers. Whatever you do, ensure the air covers the plants fully and there are no microclimates of stagnant air that form around them. Air distribution is covered in Chapter 7.

TRANSPIRATION

Q: What are some HVAC-related concerns regarding plant transpiration?

A: When plants transpire, they are releasing moisture into the air. This means the HVAC system needs to be capable of dehumidification in addition to — and, when lights are off, independent from — air conditioning.

There needs to be fine control of the vapor pressure differential to help the transpiration process along as efficiently as possible. Controlling the VPD is calculated by the grow automation system, based on the room dew point as determined via a temperature sensor.

Due to evaporative cooling, the leaf surface can be cool enough to condense moisture when transpiring. Therefore, air coverage on the plants needs to be slightly warmer than the leaves.

HUMIDITY

Q: What plant-related concerns are there regarding relative humidity?

A: Plants require a specific temperature and RH range to thrive, which depends on the strain type and the stage of growth. RH is very important because it drives the vapor pressure differential, critical to efficient transpiration. Additionally, too low RH can cause the plants to enter drought-resistant mode and slow growth. Too high RH can leave the plants open to developing mold, mildew, or viral infections.

COOLING

Q: How does an HVAC unit balance latent and sensible cooling?

A: A unitary dehumidifier can offer air conditioning with latent priority. This type of equipment would have special design elements not found in a typical air conditioner that allows it to jump between latent (air conditioning with moisture removal) and sensible (air conditioning with no moisture removal) cooling modes. If a grow room just has a regular air conditioner installed, it will need to use a secondary dehumidifier to manage humidity. You can read more about HVAC system types in Chapter 8.

DESIGN ERRORS

Q: What's the most common design error in grow rooms?

A: With no design standards yet for engineers to review, it's no surprise there are any number of mistakes that often happen. In our experience, the most common and serious is specifying and installing HVAC equipment with insufficient or no latent cooling capacity. While there is certainly a significant sensible load, it's very important to address the latent needs of the space. Another mistake, in northern climates, is using air conditioning equipment that is not designed to provide cooling during winter, something grow rooms constantly require. Read more about the challenges associated with using air conditioning equipment not designed for grow rooms in Chapter 8.

Q: How do I avoid improper equipment sizing?

A: Equipment manufacturers are best suited to provide accurate sizing. Provide them with full disclosure on factors that work into the calculation. Ensure they have been exhaustive in their consideration of all grow factors, including watering system, light type and intensity, rack type (size and tiering), plant stage, canopy density, airflow design, CO_2 design, building type, etc. More details on HVAC equipment sizing can be found in Chapter 6.

LIGHTING

Q: Why is lighting important to HVAC selection?

A: Lights are the biggest source of energy in the space. The HVAC equipment needs to remove the heat produced by the lights when they are on, while also being able to dehumidify the room without over-cooling when the lights are off.

Q: What kind of lights should be used?

A: In choosing a lighting type, it's up to the grower based on their desired plant outcomes, as well as comfort level and trust in certain technologies. Commonly, high-pressure sodium discharge and metal-halide lights are used. There is also growing evidence that using LED may be beneficial, especially for reducing HVAC costs because they emit less heat. More on lighting can be found in Chapter 7.

INSTALLATION, START-UP, AND COMMISSIONING

Q: Where should HVAC equipment be installed?

A: It will depend on the facility exactly where the system will go and whether it will be installed indoors or outdoors. Indoor installations are usually preferred because they minimize the chance of contamination. But if installed outdoors, it is critical to ensure the unit has a sturdy, insulated cabinet construction to protect against the elements. In all cases, the unit must be installed in an area where there will be adequate space for service access.

Q: When can installed equipment be commissioned?

A: In order to properly commission equipment, it must be operating under the same load and conditions it will see during regular service. This is typically difficult to achieve prior to plants being in the space. Consult with your manufacturer for advice on creating an artificial test environment.

EQUIPMENT LONGEVITY AND MAINTENANCE

Q: How do I get the longest possible life out of my HVAC unit?

A: A good-quality system can be expected to last at least 10 years but can last twice that or longer if well maintained, which includes regular changing of the air filters and cleaning of the cabinet and coils. Following the manufacturer's guidelines and advice in Chapter 11 will put you in the best possible position for a long and trouble-free service life of your equipment.

Q: What are some basic maintenance tasks almost anyone can do?

A: Changing air filters, washing down the unit, checking for corrosion, inspecting moving parts for obstructions, and verifying that outdoor heat rejection devices do not have airflow impediments are all simple tasks that should be regularly scheduled and do not require specialized technical knowledge. See a sample maintenance schedule in Chapter 11.

Q: How often should filters be changed?

A: At least after every crop is removed from the room, along with the normal decontamination procedures. If your cultivar is particularly long in flowering or produces too much pollen, you may be required to change filters more often.

Q: Why change filters?

A: Filters keep the air inside your grow room clean and free of airborne objects. As well, they protect the fragile coils from foreign contaminants that will impede performance.

Q: Do I need HEPA air filters?

A: MERV-13 is sufficient for most grow rooms. Using a higher rating, including HEPA (which is MERV-17 and above), may not provide for more reduction in airborne contaminations and will be more expensive in energy and filter replacement costs.

GLOSSARY

Ambient Air — Characteristics of the environment. For example, temperature, relative humidity, pressure, and motion.

Air Change Rate (or turnover) — Airflow in volumetric units per hour divided by the volume of the space on which the air change rate is based (normally expressed in air changes per hour). Air changes per hour: Ventilation airflow divided by room volume. It indicates how many times, during one hour, the air volume from a space is recirculated. Grow rooms need many more air changes per hour than the typical indoor environment, about 40–50 per hour.

ASHRAE — The American Society of Heating, Refrigeration and Air Conditioning Engineers publishes a variety of standards about indoor HVAC design that many professional engineers refer to when designing new structures.

CFM — Cubic Feet per Minute. Measures volume of airflow.

Dew point — Temperature at which water vapor has reached the saturation point (100% relative humidity). Temperature of the air at which it must be cooled at constant barometric pressure for water vapor to condense. Dew point influences relative humidity and vapor pressure differential.

External Static Pressure — Resistance to airflow caused by friction in air distribution networks. Lower resistance means less energy is needed to move air.

Glycol — Clear, colorless liquid used to depress the freezing point of water for use as a secondary coolant in HVAC systems. Glycol is also used for cannabis extract as a thinning agent.

Hot Gas — Refrigerant gas in the high-pressure side of the system.

Latent Cooling — When HVAC equipment removes latent heat (reduces the moisture content) of the air passing through it under specified conditions of operation.

Latent Heat — Quantity of heat required to cause a change of state of a substance from a saturated liquid to a saturated vapor with no change in temperature, measured in Btu/lbm (J/kg).

Mixed-Light — Greenhouse that blends natural light with that of artificial sources.

OACC — Outdoor air-cooled condenser. Uses refrigerant to reject heat from the dehumidifier to the outside.

Photoperiod — The length of time plants are exposed to light.

Photosynthesis — Process of plants converting sunlight and CO_2 into food.

Photomorphogenesis — Typically described as the effect of light on a plant's development. Separate from photosynthesis, but the outcome of a plant depends on the combined effects of the two phenomena.

Re-heat Coil — Heating coil installed downstream of cooling coil.

RH — Relative humidity. A measure, expressed in percentage, of how much moisture is in the air compared to the maximum amount it could hold at the same temperature.

Saturated Air — Air that holds the maximum water vapor possible at a specified temperature and pressure; i.e., moist air in which the partial pressure of the water vapor is equal to the vapor pressure of water at the existing temperature.

Sensible Cooling — When HVAC equipment removes sensible heat from the air passing through it under specified conditions of operation but does not change the moisture content (latent heat).

Sensible Heat — The energy exchanged by a thermodynamic system that relates to a change of temperature.

Transpiration — The process of water loss via stomata, pores found on plant leaves and stems. As plants absorb water through its roots, some is used in critical life functions. Most of the leftover water is jettisoned as a vapor via transpiration. Allowing plants to transpire efficiently enables them to grow better.

Vapor Pressure — The pressure exerted by a vapor. If a vapor is kept in confinement over its liquid so that the vapor can accumulate above the liquid with the temperature constant, the vapor pressure reaches a maximum called the saturated vapor pressure.

Vapor Pressure Differential (VPD) — Every temperature has a dew point, and every dew point has a vapor pressure. For ideal plant conditions, the HVAC system needs to ensure the vapor pressure of the leaf surface is greater than that of the surrounding air. This ensures that the plant will always be able to transpire efficiently. Usually VPD is influenced by changing the relative humidity of surrounding air.

Water-Cooled System — An HVAC setup where refrigerant is kept in a sealed circuit within the unit and heat is rejected outside using water as a secondary heat exchange fluid. Usually glycol is mixed with the water to prevent freezing.

Wavelength — Defines the colour of light within the electromagnetic spectrum, expressed in nanometers of length. The visible spectrum of light falls within about 380–740 nanometers. The shorter the wavelength, the higher the frequency and energy.

Some definitions via ASHRAE.

RESOURCES

We've compiled a variety of free online resources from the Agronomic IQ and Quest websites to help guide readers on their journey to **Getting Grow Rooms Right**.

AGRONOMIC IQ

The Agronomic IQ Evolution Series

Designed from the ground up to provide the ultimate solution for the vast majority of grow rooms, the Evolution Series answers every one of the most critical grow room requirements.

AgronomicIQ.com/evolution-series

Agronomic IQ Compressor Wall Technology

Ensuring high air flow in a revolutionary design, our Compressor Wall technology takes a modular, scalable, and redundant approach to dehumidification like nothing else in the market.

AgronomicIQ.com/compressor-wall

GrowSentry™ Performance Monitoring

Learn how GrowSentry™ technology provides real peace of mind for growers with internet monitoring and remote control, sending performance data every 60 seconds, 24 hours a day, 7 days a week.

AgronomicIQ.com/GrowSentry

Full Product Brochure

Download the full product brochure to find the right equipment from the Agronomic IQ series, built specifically to meet the exacting requirements of growing cannabis for every size of grow facility.

AgronomicIQ.com/product-brochure

Load Selection Sheet

Complete the application details on this load selection sheet such as room basics, temperature, lighting, and the active grow area to help determine the right equipment for each room.

AgronomicIQ.com/load-selection-sheet

The 3 Biggest Challenges

Discover the 3 biggest challenges of modern day grow rooms, and the common mistakes that growers make when selecting HVAC solutions.

AgronomicIQ.com/three-biggest-challenges

Top 10 Reasons

Learn the truth about growing cannabis and the top 10 reasons why choosing the right system and HVAC partner is fundamental to successful grow room operations.

AgronomicIQ.com/top-ten-reasons

Stay Informed

Get important news, the latest trends, and best practices to create the optimal grow room temperature and humidity control environment, delivered directly to your inbox.

AgronomicIQ.com/newsletter

Dehumidified Air Services

Dehumidified Air Services is a coast-to-coast service network of local customer support technicians. Backed by real-time remote monitoring technology and with direct access to the engineers who designed Agronomic IQ dehumidifiers, Dehumidified Air Services is the only organization in North America that has the scale and expertise to deliver trouble-free dehumidification and unparalleled customer service.

https://dehumidifiedairservices.com/

QUEST

Product Manuals
Download product manuals and specification sheets for the Quest 506 and 876 high capacity dehumidifiers, designed with efficiency and growers in mind.

QuestClimate.com/manuals

The Quest Blog
Take control of your environment with informative articles for growers on the Quest blog.

QuestClimate.com/blog

FAQs
Get answers to the most frequently asked questions about relative humidity, dew point, air flow, and more.

QuestClimate.com/frequently-asked-questions

HOW TO REACH US

With over 80 combined years of experience in the dehumidification industry, it's no wonder grow room professionals turn to and trust Agronomic IQ and Quest dehumidification expertise and equipment. We'd love to discuss your project requirements.

Contact@AgronomicIQ.com
1.833.327.2447

Sales@QuestClimate.com
1.877.420.1330

GET YOUR BONUS CHAPTER:

FILTRATION AND ODOR MANAGEMENT

With modern-day grow rooms, the new reality is scale, and with more scale, naturally occurring chemicals and other compounds used in cannabis production means more odors.

As HVAC systems are not typically designed to eliminate odor, this bonus chapter provides alternatives to activated carbon filtration to help mitigate odors effectively.

AgronomicIQ.com/bookbonus

NOTES

CHAPTER 1

[1]Grand View Research. "Legal Marijuana Market Worth $66.3 Billion By 2025." News release, May 2019. www.grandviewresearch.com. Accessed June 2019. https://www.grandviewresearch.com/press-release/global-legal-marijuana-market.

[2]Small, E., T. Pocock, and P. B. Cavers. "The Biology of Canadian Weeds. 119. Cannabis Sativa L." *Canadian Journal of Plant Science* 83, no. 1 (2003): 217–37. Accessed July 2019. doi:10.4141/p02–021.

[3]Warf, Barney. "High Points: An Historical Geography of Cannabis." Geographical Review 104, no. 4 (2014): 414–38. Accessed June 19, 2019. doi:10.1111/j.1931-0846.2014.12038.x.

[4]Dickenson, Victoria. "Cartier, Champlain, and the Fruits of the New World." *Scientia Canadensis: Canadian Journal of the History of Science, Technology and Medicine* 31, no. 1–2 (2008): 27. Accessed June 19, 2019. doi:10.7202/019753ar.

[5]Kelly, Annie. "Hemp Is at Hand." *The Guardian* (London). September 27, 2006. Accessed June 19, 2019. https://www.theguardian.com/environment/2006/sep/27/society.conservationandendangeredspecies.

[6]Abel, Ernest L. *Marihuana: The First Twelve Thousand Years.* New York: Springer Science Business Media, 1980. Accessed June 19, 2019. http://www.herbmuseum.ca/content/hemp-plant-canada.

[7]Canada. Library of Parliament. Law and Government Division. *Historical and Cultural Uses of Cannabis and the Canadian "Marijuana Clash"*. By Leah Spicer. Prepared for The Senate Special Committee on Illegal Drugs. April 12, 2002. Accessed June 19, 2019. https://sencanada.ca/content/sen/committee/371/ille/library/spicer-e.htm.

[8]Kobson, Jay. "The Real Dope on Gene Krupa's Narcotics Conviction." Lowdown magazine via Drummerman.net. 2004. Accessed July 16, 2019. http://www.drummerman.net/drugbust.html.

(Original article from late 1940s Lowdown magazine, republished in 2004 on drummerman.net.)

[9]Brown, Ian. "A Biography of Cannabis." *Globe and Mail*, July 1, 2018. Accessed June 19, 2019. https://www.theglobeandmail.com/cannabis/article-a-biography-of-cannabis/.

[10]Elsohly, Mahmoud A., Zlatko Mehmedic, Susan Foster, Chandrani Gon, Suman Chandra, and James C. Church. "Changes in Cannabis Potency Over the Last 2 Decades (1995–2014): Analysis

of Current Data in the United States." *Biological Psychiatry* 79, no. 7 (April 1, 2016): 613–19. Accessed June 20, 2019. doi:10.1016/j.biopsych.2016.01.004.

[11]Jourabchi, Massoud, and Maggie Lahet. *Electrical Load Impacts of Indoor Commercial Cannabis Production*. PDF. Northwest Power and Conservation Council, September 9, 2014. Accessed June 20, 2019. https://www.nwcouncil.org/sites/default/files/p7.pdf

CHAPTER 3

[12]U.S. Oregon Liquor Control Commission. *2019 Recreational Marijuana Supply and Demand Legislative Report*. By Steve Marks. January 31, 2019. Accessed June 17, 2019.

[13]Sevcenko, Melanie. "Two Months after Oregon Legalization, Pot Saturation Sends Profits up in Smoke." *The Guardian*, November 21, 2015. Accessed June 2019. https://www.theguardian.com/us-news/2015/nov/21/oregon-cannabis-legalization-medical-marijuana-dying-market.

[14]Orens, Adam, Miles Light, Brian Lewandowski, Jacob Rowberry, and Clinton Saloga. *Market Size and Demand for Marijuana in Colorado 2017 Market Update*. Report. Marijuana Policy Group and University of Colorado Boulder, Leeds School of Business, Business Research Division. Prepared for the Colorado Department of Revenue. August 2018. Accessed June 28, 2019.

[15]Goldberg, Jennifer. "Parents Who Smoke Pot." *Today's Parent*, April 20, 2018. Accessed July 2, 2019. https://www.todaysparent.com/family/parenting/parents-who-smoke-pot/.

[16]Miner and Co. "The New Cannabis Consumer — Stoners No More." News release, November 2016. Accessed July 2, 2019. https://www.minerandcostudio.com/a-new-class-of-cannabis-consumers.

[17]Statistics Canada. *National Cannabis Survey, First Quarter 2019*. May 2, 2019. Accessed July 2, 2019. https://www150.statcan.gc.ca/n1/daily-quotidien/190502/dq190502a-eng.htm.

[18]*Aphria Investor Presentation*. PDF. Aphria Inc., April 2019. Accessed July 2, 2019.

[19]"New Coke — Top 10 Bad Beverage Ideas." *Time*. Accessed July 17, 2019. http://content.time.com/time/specials/packages/article/0,28804,1913612_1913610_1913608,00.html.

[20]*Supreme Cannabis Company Investor Presentation*. PDF. Supreme Cannabis Co., June 2019.

[21]Report. *Recreational Marijuana: Insights and Opportunities*. Deloitte. Accessed July 2019. https://www2.deloitte.com/content/dam/Deloitte/

ca/Documents/Analytics/ca-en-analytics-DELOITTE Recreational Marijuana POV - ENGLISH FINAL AODA.pdf.

CHAPTER 4

[22]Ligaya, Armina. "Time Running out for Firms to Grow Pot Outdoors as They Await Licenses." *The Canadian Press/Canadian Business*, May 16, 2019. Accessed July 2, 2019. https://www.canadianbusiness.com/business-news/time-running-out-for-firms-to-grow-pot-outdoors-as-they-await-licenses/.

[23]Dunham, Jackie, and Zayn Jinah. "Canada's Largest Outdoor Cannabis Farm Ready for Growth." *CTV News*, May 29, 2019. Accessed July 17, 2019. https://www.ctvnews.ca/canada/canada-s-largest-outdoor-cannabis-farm-ready-for-growth-1.4441978.

[24]Chen, Rachel. "In or Out? Is Cannabis Grown Indoors Better than Weed Grown Outdoors?" *The Growth Op*, Postmedia, April 23, 2019. Accessed July 17, 2019. https://www.thegrowthop.com/cannabis-business/cannabis-experts/in-or-out-is-cannabis-grown-indoors-better-than-weed-grown-outdoors.

[25]Canopy Growth Corporation. "Canopy Growth Adds Substantial Production Capacity in Canada after Receiving Licence for New Outdoor Site." News release, June 24, 2019. Yahoo via Cision. Accessed July 17, 2019. https://finance.yahoo.com/news/canopy-growth-adds-substantial-production-110000501.html.

[26]George-Cosh, David. "'We Need to Try Everything': Canopy Tests Growing Pot Outdoors." *BNN Bloomberg*, June 25, 2019. Accessed July 2, 2019. https://www.bnnbloomberg.ca/we-need-to-try-everything-canopy-tests-growing-pot-outdoors-1.1278278.

[27]"What Is a Mother Plant?" *Aurora Cannabis* (blog), May 13, 2018. Accessed June 27, 2019. https://www.auroramj.com/blog/2018/05/13/what-is-a-mother-plant/.

[28]*CANNABIS: Propagation — Cloning Methods for Commercial Growers*. PDF. Conviron, December 2017.

CHAPTER 7

[29]Bilodeau, Samuel Eichhorn, Bo-Sen Wu, Anne-Sophie Rufyikiri, Sarah Macpherson, and Mark Lefsrud. "An Update on Plant Photobiology and Implications for Cannabis Production." *Frontiers in Plant Science* 10 (March 29, 2019). Accessed July 4, 2019. doi:10.3389/fpls.2019.00296.

[30]"LED Lighting & Photosynthesis Guide." Fluence Bioengineering. Accessed July 17, 2019. https://fluence.science/science/photosynthesis-guide/.

[31]Yorio, Neil C., Gregory D. Goins, Hollie R. Kagie, Raymond M. Wheeler, and John C. Sager. "Improving Spinach, Radish, and Lettuce Growth under Red Light-emitting Diodes (LEDs) with Blue Light Supplementation." *HortScience* 36, no. 2 (April 2001): 380–83. doi:10.21273/hortsci.36.2.380.

[32]Magagnini, Gianmaria, Gianpaolo Grassi, and Stiina Kotiranta. "The Effect of Light Spectrum on the Morphology and Cannabinoid Content of Cannabis Sativa L." *Medical Cannabis and Cannabinoids* 1, no. 1 (June 12, 2018): 19–27. Accessed July 4, 2019. doi:10.1159/000489030.

[33]Snowden, M. Chase, Kevin R. Cope, and Bruce Bugbee. "Sensitivity of Seven Diverse Species to Blue and Green Light: Interactions with Photon Flux." *Plos One* 11, no. 10 (October 05, 2016). Accessed July 4, 2019. doi:10.1371/journal.pone.0163121.

[34]Kaiser, Elias, Kees Weerheim, Rachel Schipper, and Janneke A. Dieleman. "Partial replacement of red and blue by green light increases biomass and yield in tomato." *Scientia Horticulturae* 249 (2019): 271. *Academic OneFile* (accessed July 17, 2019).

[35]Eaves, James, Stephen Eaves, Chad Morphy, and Chris Murray. "The Impact of Light Intensity and Spectrum-Tuning on Cannabis Yields." *SSRN Electronic Journal*, January 15, 2019. Accessed July 17, 2019. doi:10.2139/ssrn.3310456.